Hamster
Sickness (
Health

Sheila Adby
and
Dan O Neill MVB BSc(Hons) MRCVS

To Kevin
    with lots of love
        from

            Sheila

www.capallbann.co.uk

Hamsters in Sickness and in Health

Cover design by Paul Mason
Cartoons by Pete Adby
Illustrations by Emily Watkins

Published by:

Capall Bann Publishing
Auton Farm
Milverton
Somerset
TA4 1NE

In memory of Flossy, Wheelie
and all my other hamsters who
inspired the writing of this book

Sheila Adby

For my three eternal hamsters:
Alistair, Megan and Clodagh

Dan O Neill

Contents

Acknowledgements

We are indebted to many people for helping make this book with contributions of expert advice and encouragement.

We would especially like to thank the following:

Christopher Day MA VetMB CertIAVH Vet FFHom MRCVS, who is a founder member of the British Association for Homeopathic Veterinary Surgeons. He runs the Alternative Veterinary Medicine Centre in rural South Oxfordshire. We are grateful to him for providing the homeopathic information contained in this book.

Elaine Quincey, known locally as 'the hamster lady', has been breeding and judging hamsters for more than twenty years. She kindly allowed a visit to meet all her hamsters and answer an infinite number of questions.

Jacky Carter who operates a rescue and re-homing service for hamsters and other small animals not only offered her advice and expertise but also 'loaned' out hamsters for observation purposes.

Debbie Hillman Dip ION, a nutritional therapist, was given the unusual task of suggesting a diabetic diet for dwarf hamsters. She has produced comprehensive and helpful advice for ensuring these little creatures are given a well balanced diet.

Ron Rees Davies BVSc CertZooMed MRCVS, a veterinary surgeon specialising in exotic pet species, Keith Ward, pet shop owner, Yvonne Arrow, Wendy Barry and Susan Washbrook who proof read the book and offered helpful advice.

Dr Aidan P Foster, Lecturer in Veterinary Dermatology, Bristol University, who provided state-of-art information on Polyoma Virus.

Thanks also to Pete Adby and Emily Watkins for their wonderful drawings.

Among the many companies who contributed information, special thanks to Supreme Petfoods Ltd, Bayer UK Ltd, Vetoquinol Ltd and Schering Plough Ltd.

A big thank you to everyone else who provided helpful tips, hamster stories, advice, support and encouragement in the writing of this book.

Foreword

"This exciting new book is a joy to read. It is refreshing to find a book that goes into such depth on hamster health matters.

I believe the information in this book will be of great value to both the novice hamster owner and the experienced breeder.

This book has been written with care and compassion for these wonderful creatures."

Wendy Barry
Secretary of the British Hamster Association

About the Authors

Sheila Adby lives with Jasper, her house bunny, and an ever-increasing number of hamsters and gerbils. Her fascination with these small creatures started some seven years ago when she offered to look after her niece's gerbil while she was on holiday. Since then she has offered her home to many unwanted and unloved hamsters and gerbils. As a qualified acupuncturist she has a particular interest in alternative medicine and looking at more natural ways of treating animals.

Dan O Neill qualified in 1987 with a first class honours veterinary degree from Dublin Veterinary College and in 1991 with a first class honours pharmacology degree from University College Dublin. After spells of university lecturing, corporate consultancy and large animal practice, he has run his own small animal and exotics veterinary practice in Petts Wood, Kent since 1996. He is married with three children and a household of varied pets.

Introduction

It's late one evening and your hamster still hasn't made an appearance. After a while you realise there is something very wrong but you're not sure what to do. Your hamster looks poorly, definitely not its usual self. You wonder whether to make an emergency call to the vet, try to treat the condition yourself or wait and see if your hamster is still alive in the morning before deciding what to do. Hopefully this book will help in such a dilemma.

As a hamster owner, there are a number of things you can do to help your pet and ensure it has a good life. This involves giving it the right type of housing, bedding, food and attention. In addition, it is important to know when you need to take it to the vet or when you can treat it at home.

This book aims to give an overview of what is involved in keeping a hamster whether you are a very beginner who is just discovering how much fun they are or someone who has kept them for many years. It also offers advice on first aid treatments and alternative remedies that can play an important part in your hamster's life.

All the information in this book is based on personal experience of keeping and treating hamsters. Due to a dearth of official research into the treatment of these small animals, some of the suggested treatments given are purely based on word of mouth and the experience of people who have kept hamsters for many years.

Remember, if you are in doubt about the health of your hamster, get veterinary advice quickly as this could mean the difference between life and death for them.

Hamsters are great fun to keep as pets, but sadly some get ill or need special attention. The important lesson is that the more knowledge you possess, then the better the quality of life will be for your hamsters in sickness and in health.

Chapter 1

Your First Hamster

Pets may be either a planned or an impulse purchase. An unexpected visit with your children to a pet shop or garden centre may lead to many happy years of pet ownership but if you get it wrong, it could lead to a lot of heartache. Once a child has seen a pet they like, especially once they've handled it, it can be extremely difficult for a parent to refuse them. Forward planning is vital in making the right choice.

Advice for a parent
Think carefully about taking on any pet for a child. Children definitely benefit from the responsibility of owning and caring for a pet of their own but the reality is that there are a lot of unwanted and neglected pets in this world. Many such pets are the leftovers after the honeymoon period of childhood pet ownership has ended.

Having decided to get a pet for your child, visit the pet shop beforehand on your own to investigate the choice of pets available. You can then steer your child in the right direction during the complete family visit. Otherwise you might go home with a completely different pet than expected!

It is easy to think small animals such as hamsters need little care but nothing could be further from the truth. Consider what you will do if your child decides they do not like the pet after a short time. Syrian (Golden) hamsters live around 18-30 months, dwarf hamsters can live 2 years and Chinese hamsters for even longer. They will need feeding daily, to be cleaned out regularly, given sufficient exercise and taken to the vet if they become sick. Try to prepare your children for this in advance. Young children often lose interest in them once the novelty has worn off and the reality of what is involved in taking care of them sinks in.

There are a number of other points that need to be considered carefully in advance:

Time commitment - not just in feeding and cleaning out, but also human daily interaction, which after all, is the reason you got the hamster in the first place. Longhaired hamsters will also need regular grooming.

Other Pets - having a hamster in a house full of cats is asking for trouble. Whilst it need not be a problem, children need to understand that hamsters have to be kept safely away from other animals and when handling them, other pets must be banned from the room.

Weekly costs - In addition to the initial outlay on a cage or tank, there are weekly costs for wood chippings, bedding and food. Toys will also need to be provided.

Veterinary fees - at some stage during its life, a hamster may need to see the vet, even if it is just for nail and teeth trimming. Should extensive surgery be required, then the veterinary fees could be several times the initial cost of the hamster. Are you prepared to pay for this?

Health Issues - there are possible human health hazards to keeping pets, even small caged ones, as well as all the well-documented benefits. The commonest problem is bite injuries to fingers poked through the bars of cages or following thoughtless handling of sleepy hamsters.

Immuno-compromised persons may be susceptible to picking up pathogenic organisms from their pet. People with asthma or other allergies may find that the presence of a pet aggravates their condition.

Commitment - the well-known saying that 'A pet is for life, not just for Christmas' applies as much to small pets as to larger ones. Of course their life span is that much shorter than dogs and cats, but having purchased a pet it is vital that they are given the best possible quality of life, even if it is only for a couple of years.

Holiday arrangements - whilst it is acceptable to leave your hamster alone over night provided it has been given sufficient food and water, it will be necessary to arrange for someone to look after it if you are away for any longer.

Smells - providing they are cleaned out regularly, hamsters are not smelly pets. However, some individuals with a very sensitive sense of smell may find the odours more noticeable and disagreeable.

Syrian, Russian, Chinese or Roborovski hamster?
The most commonly found hamster in pet shops is the Syrian hamster, formerly known as the Golden hamster. These are available as short haired or longhaired in a variety of colours. Syrian hamsters are the largest of the common hamsters. They are the easiest to handle and one-to-one relationships with their owners often develop into something very special.

Russian dwarf hamsters are considerably smaller than Syrians, Campbells being the most likely one you will find for sale in a pet shop. They are very territorial and have quite different temperaments from other dwarf varieties. They have a reputation for biting, although this is often when being picked up from the nest. Once out of the tank they tend to be

Syrian

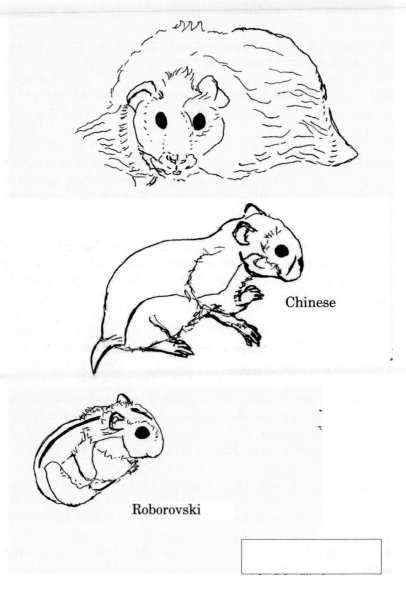

Chinese

Roborovski

more placid. Campbells are prone to a disease called diabetes, which tends to run in families and can be triggered by stress. They have also been known to develop glaucoma.

Another variety of Russian dwarf hamster is the Winter White. Not quite as territorial as Campbells, they are easier to handle and unlikely to bite. They can easily be confused with Campbells as they are physically similar but the Winter Whites are slightly smaller and have thicker fur. The fur of a 'normal' coloured Winter White is more greyish black, compared with the tan shade of a Campbell.

Chinese hamsters are not commonly found in pet shops in contrast to Syrians or Campbells. They have a good temperament and when handled tend to wrap themselves round your finger. They are approximately 7-9 cm when fully grown, look quite mouse-like and have a slightly longer tail than the Syrian and Russian dwarfs. On the whole, they tend to be healthy.

Roborovski hamsters, who originate from Mongolia, are the smallest of the dwarf hamsters, measuring only about 4cm when fully grown. They like to live in colonies and the introduction of new individuals to an established family unit is very difficult. Roborovski's are great fun to have in a colony but it will be necessary to separate them should fighting occur. They are very agile and quite difficult to handle and therefore not necessarily ideal for children. They are one of the healthier of the hamster varieties.

Although all these hamsters are similar-looking small furry creatures, their behaviour and requirements are quite different. Syrian hamsters are solitary and nocturnal; often they do not rally round until well into the evening when they come out for food and exercise. Although Syrian hamsters do sometimes surface during the day, normally it is just to get food and often they are not in the mood for being handled. If you disturb them when they are sleeping they tend to grind their teeth to warn you off or they might even try to bite. Younger children who go to bed in the early evening might not get much of a chance to interact with their pet unless the hamster has been trained to wake earlier in the day. Their nocturnal nature needs to be borne in mind when deciding on the location of the cage as hamsters can make quite a lot of noise when exercising in their wheels in the middle of the night.

Dwarf hamsters and Chinese hamsters, on the other hand, whilst tending to be more active in the evenings, can go through phases of activity and sleep throughout the day and night. They tend to be much faster than Syrian hamsters to handle, but providing they have been tamed from an early age, they can be handled. Small children, however, should be supervised when playing with them.

Male or Female/Long or short haired?
Females are great fun and tend to have stronger personalities than males and make more interesting pets. Male Syrian hamsters can be extremely placid and often easier to handle than females and are therefore often recommended for children who have never handled a small animal before. Longhaired hamsters will need regular grooming to help keep their coat in good condition. It is the male Syrian hamster who has the long skirt that will need grooming to prevent it getting matted and caught up with bedding and wood chippings. Consideration will also need to be given to the type of wheel given to them as it is possible for them to get their long hair caught in the central spoke of some wheels. (See Chapter 3)

Where should you purchase your hamster?

When purchasing a hamster from a pet shop, ensure that the shop is reputable. Check to see how well the pets have been looked after, that their cages are clean and there are no obvious signs of neglect of any of the animals or bad smells. Should you be worried that a pet shop is not correctly caring for their animals, it can be reported to the RSPCA. Look for pet shops that offer a 'follow up' service, whereby a month or two after homing one of their pets, you are invited to return it to the shop for a check up. During this visit some will even award a Pet Care Certificate to the pet owner, which is further encouragement for children to take responsibility for their hamster.

The entire responsibility for providing you with the best pet to fulfil your needs does not rest solely with the pet shop but is shared equally between you both. Before visiting the pet shop (especially with a child), you should have carried out some basic research on the types of pets available, their needs, lifespan, suitability for your requirements, odour, cost, etc. Your local library, your veterinary surgeon or the Internet are good places to begin as well as discussing pet ownership with people who already own the type of pet that interests you.

Hand tamed hamsters are often best for children. Whilst it is possible to tame most hamsters, if the hamster has already been hand tamed it will be a lot easier to handle immediately and less likely to bite. Once bitten by their pet, children often lose interest in them or become permanently afraid of them resulting in a parent left with an unwanted pet and a difficult decision as to what to do with it.

Hamsters bred by friends often make good pets, as they would have been handled from an early age and are therefore used to being picked up. This also makes possible an assessment of the likely future temperament of the hamster by examination of the behaviour of the parents since vicious traits are often hereditary.

You may wish to consider homing a hamster from a pet rescue centre. A large number of unwanted and abandoned hamsters go to rescue centres, some of which may already be pregnant. These are sometimes fostered out until their offspring reach 4-5 weeks old, during which time many will have been handled in order to tame them and will make excellent pets.

Alternatively, you can purchase your hamster from a local breeder. The British Hamster Association (address given in Chapter 10) maintains a register of breeders and can provide details upon request.

What to look for when purchasing a hamster
Since Syrian hamsters are nocturnal, they should be sleeping when you see them in the pet shop. Those that are seen climbing the cage or foraging for food during the day may be slightly hyperactive or do not feel comfortable in their surroundings. Females are often more active than males and awaken more frequently during the day, normally to investigate any sounds or smells outside the cage. A hamster that has just been woken from a deep sleep in order to be handled will not be fully awake and alert and will be irritable. To avoid being bitten, do not be tempted to stroke the hamster through the cage bars or to pick it up out of the nest if it is sleeping - this is a job for the sales assistant!

If you are buying more than one dwarf or Chinese hamster, look for signs of injuries that might have resulted from siblings picking on them. Otherwise you might find yourself either having to separate them early on or making a trip to the vet sooner rather than later for medical advice.

"Would you like to pick out the hamster you like?" asked the sales assistant. Being naïve, I agreed and a split second later saw a hamster dangling from my hand and my blood dripping on the shop floor. My first experience of hamsters resulted in a visit to the hospital for a tetanus jab! Fortunately, I wasn't put off by this experience and a week later I met Barney, a very friendly hand tamed Syrian, who was to become my first hamster and the start of my fascination and love for these little creatures.

In all cases the hamster's eyes should be bright, there should be no obvious signs of any skin or ear problems and their fur should be in good condition.

How many hamsters should you purchase?
Syrian hamsters must be kept alone. Although the pet shop may keep several in a cage together, they are probably still quite young, approximately 6 weeks old. They should, however, be separated into single sexed cages when they are 4 weeks old. They can then be kept in single sexed cages for another two weeks but after this they should be separated to avoid fighting or in some cases killing each other. If you do decide to get two Syrians, you will have to double all your initial and ongoing costs.

Campbells prefer to live together in a colony but will need to be separated should fighting occur. Unless you are planning on breeding them ensure that the sex of each one is checked carefully. The same applies to Roborovski hamsters. Do not under any circumstances, however, mix these two breeds.

It is possible to keep Winter Whites in either same-sex or different-sex pairs. It can be very difficult to re-introduce Winter Whites once separated. Therefore only separate them if they are really fighting and one has been injured or is likely to be. They will squabble from time to time but they often remain friends. They are easier to handle than Campbells, and tend not to bite. Campbells and Winter White hamsters are extremely vocal and this should not be confused with serious fighting. Ensuring there are plenty of toys and places for your hamsters to hide within the cage will help prevent fighting. Should fighting still occur, a small amount of perfume or aftershave can be dabbed on the outside base of the cage daily for 1-2 weeks. This will help disguise their scent and help to stop them fighting.

Chinese hamsters can also be kept in pairs or in colonies. Sometimes the female will pick on the male and this is more common if she is pregnant. In the event of fighting, it will be necessary to separate them.

A word of warning needs to be given regarding the sexing of young hamsters. Most hamsters can be sexed from a few weeks old, especially when there are both sexes present to aid differentiation of males from females. However, some pet shops are not confident in their ability to safely sex such small animals and, in many ways, it is better for the pet shop to admit they do not know what sex the hamster is, rather than to give false information. However, should you find you have been given the wrong information concerning the sex of your hamster, you may discover some of your 'males' becoming pregnant. It is worth checking in advance that the shop will accept back any resultant babies if necessary. This also applies to hamsters purchased from breeders or rescue centres.

Introducing hamsters at a later date
It is extremely difficult to introduce hamsters to an established colony at a later date and it is therefore recommended that if you wish to try to keep more than one dwarf hamster or Chinese hamster in a tank that you do so from outset. These creatures are very territorial and do not take kindly to the

arrival of a new hamster. This also applies when trying to mate two hamsters as even then the female might attack the male.

Even when a colony has grown up together there is still no guarantee that they will not suddenly turn on one of the group. After a colony decides to pick on a hamster they tend not to kill it outright. Instead, they keep attacking it and continually biting it until, eventually, it will die if it is not removed. This is an extremely distressing situation. Should you notice your hamsters picking on one individual, monitor the situation very closely and remove it if you feel it is at risk. Be careful, however, not to over-react to simple squabbles that are common only to see the same hamsters curled up together later that same day, back to being the best of friends. Chinese hamsters from different litters can sometimes be introduced to one another up to 4 weeks old but after this period it is extremely difficult. When introducing a female to a male, it is important that they are closely monitored for any signs of aggression.

Whilst adult Syrian hamsters must be kept on their own, do not underestimate friendships between two hamsters living in cages side by side. They are fully aware of their neighbours due to their excellent sense of smell. They get used to the position of their cages and if there is another hamster living next door, they will often sniff each other through the bars.

> *Wheelie was a rescue hamster, found in a black sack that had been thrown into a dustbin. She lived happily for a year in a new home, with her cage situated next to Scruffy, a rather sad looking hamster with an equally sorry tale to tell. The pair were inseparable. Although they never actually met outside of their cages they would spend their evenings chewing their bars together and rubbing noses. Scruffy even went so far as to relocate his nest in his cage so it was*

alongside Wheelie's. That way, he knew when she was awake and as soon as she stirred he would get out of his nest to see her. Sadly Wheelie became ill and had to be put to sleep. Scruffy clearly missed her and within one week he suffered a stroke and died - possibly from a broken heart.

Reintroduction of hamsters

Problems often occur when one hamster from a colony becomes ill and needs treatment. If you are applying a strong smelling cream to one of the hamsters, it is advisable to also apply a very small amount to the coats of the others in the colony too. This prevents one hamster being singled out by the others on the basis of odour from either the medication or human hands. Should one undergo surgery it is worth bearing in mind that the smell of the anaesthetic and antiseptics alone could cause the others to pick on it. In addition, to avoid the stitches being removed by others in the colony, you may need to keep the hamster in a separate tank for a few days whilst the wound heals. In such an event, swap some of the bedding between the cages on a daily basis to allow the others in the colony to recognise and accept any new smells. When you do try to reintroduce them a few days later monitor closely and remove them from the tank if there are any signs of aggression from the other hamsters. Campbells are easier to re-introduce but, even then, there is no guarantee that the others will accept them. The moral is therefore to only separate hamsters when absolutely necessary to avoid being faced with extra solitary individuals and the need for provision of additional housing for them.

Should you need to take a dwarf or Chinese hamster to the vet, depending on the type of illness, it is worth considering taking the entire colony for a check up even when only one seems ill. This reduces the risk of rejection of the sick individual by the rest of the colony on return due to any acquired scents during the visit. Secondly, illnesses can affect a whole colony or be hereditary, so your vet will be able to ascertain how many in the colony are affected. In the event of your colony being kept in a glass tank, for safety purposes, it might be necessary to transport them in a carry case.

Making a room hamster-proof
These little creatures are great escapologists. If a cage door is left open or is broken, they will take the opportunity to make a bid for freedom. Therefore, when deciding in which room to site their cage, ensure first that any nooks or crannies in the room and any gaps in the skirting board are blocked. Also ensure any electrical or phone cables are out of reach as hamsters can easily gnaw through these when they are on the loose. It is worth noting that hamsters can climb curtains and escape out of open windows.

The belief is that hamsters are colour blind. However, in some colonies of Campbells it has been found that all the hamsters of one particular colour are picked on by the others. Once they have been forced out of the colony or killed, it has been known for the colony to then pick on another colour.

Chapter 2

Housing and Hygiene

It is easy to become extremely confused when deciding on a cage for a new hamster. There are so many variables; single tier, multiple tier, wire cages, glass tanks, plastic tanks, multi-coloured tanks with tubes and attachments, and so on. The prices also vary dramatically from one type to another and from one brand to another.

However, the most important point to remember is that regardless of the design you choose, it needs to be big enough and suitable for the type of hamster or hamsters that will be living there. This might sound obvious, but what might be suitable for a Syrian hamster might not be suitable for a dwarf hamster. In short, once you have ascertained the most appropriate type of housing required, it is best to get the biggest cage/tank you can fit in your house or that you can afford as this will give your pet plenty of space to run around as well as allowing room for their toys.

Points to consider when purchasing a cage

Is the home going to be for one or more hamsters?

What breed of hamster will live there?

How big will the hamster grow? What might be suitable for them as a 6-week-old may not be big enough when they have reached adulthood.

What are their requirements likely to be?

How much space is there in my house to fit the cage?

Can the cage system be expanded at a later date?

Am I likely to breed more hamsters?

How much am I prepared to spend?

How easy is it to clean out?

How easy is it for the hamster to escape from?

Different needs of different breeds

Syrian hamsters are solitary animals and need individual homes. Some can grow quite large. They like to climb and exercise therefore wire cages are ideal for them. The majority of wheels that come already fitted in cages are too small for adult Syrians and will need to be changed later. Check that there is enough room for a jumbo wheel to be fitted once the hamster has out-grown the small wheel.

The small plastic houses that often come inside wire cages are not recommended for Syrians. These houses tend to collect condensation, even if the roof has been removed, and hoarded food will quickly go mouldy. These houses are more suitable for the dwarf hamster varieties.

Tubular tanks look fun but make sure there will be sufficient ventilation for your hamster and that there is enough room for them to move about. Some tubes are quite narrow, especially where there is a junction and Syrian hamsters might have difficulty getting through. Also consider the accessibility to food supplies. As your hamster gets older, or perhaps develops some medical problems, climbing vertically up tubes to gain access to food might be difficult. Also ensure that if your hamster has babies inside this type of tank, food and water supplies are easily accessible, as the young offspring would be unable to climb up tubes in search of it. Ventilation is also severely reduced in this type of housing,

30

which can result in respiratory problems for the inhabitants. Some of the tubular houses are better as a play area for your hamster, rather than as living accommodation.

Dwarf and Chinese hamsters are often kept in colonies. A tank is ideal for them and provides plenty of room for toys. They love tubes and obstacles to climb over or walk through. Some of the tubular tanks can also be fun for them but bear in mind that you will need to dismantle each section in order to clean it out on a weekly basis so there is a high level of maintenance work required. Also ensure the vertical tube has ridges inside in order for them to be able to get a foothold when climbing. It might be necessary to insert a mouse ladder inside the tubes. If you are keeping several Campbells or Roborovski hamsters ensure the tank is big enough. This is especially important if you are breeding them because the dominant female may cannibalise her young if she feels that the cage is too small for the colony.

Fish tanks are not suitable for hamsters due to their limited ventilation. There are many different types of glass and plastic tanks specifically designed for hamsters that overcome these ventilation problems.

Carry cases
Should your hamster need to be taken to the vet at any time, it might not be possible for you to take them in their cage or tank - especially if the tank is glass. Therefore, it is a good idea to purchase a carry case. These should only be used in the short

31

term as a means of transportation as they are too small to keep hamsters in for any protracted length of time. They are also ideal for safe storage of your hamster(s) while cleaning out the main home.

Location of housing

Do not put any cages or tanks close to windows or in conservatories. Whilst it may seem idyllic to have the cage on a windowsill, it may become too hot and result in a hamster suffering a heat stroke. Cages should be kept in well-ventilated rooms. If the room is prone to direct sunlight, blinds or curtains should be drawn to protect the cages from excessive heat, especially if you are keeping your pets in glass or plastic tanks that already suffer from low ventilation. Cages should also be in draught free locations and safely positioned away from any other pets in the house e.g. cats and dogs.

A sudden drop in temperature can cause hamsters to hibernate so a fairly consistent temperature should be maintained, the ideal temperature being between 65-70°F (18.3-21.1°C). Remember to never bury a 'dead' hamster as it might just be hibernating (see Chapter 7 for more information on hibernating hamsters).

Ideally cages should not be sited in bedrooms. This is partly due to the noise nuisance from hamsters running in their wheels during the night but also to minimise risks of allergic or irritant reactions in children because of such close proximity of the child to the pet and its bedding for long periods during the night. Respiratory problems may also result for the hamsters from exposure to airborne irritants such as talcum powder, deodorants and perfumes.

There are also risks with situating a hamster cage in a garage. Firstly, there is the problem of wildly fluctuating temperatures with the summers getting too hot while the winters may bring freezing temperatures due to the absence of central heating. Secondly, these little creatures are very sensitive to smells and exposure to car fumes and other garage solvents can make them very sick. It is also worth noting that most hamsters are very sociable and love human company. It is important, therefore, to place their cage where they can easily interact with their owners every day, even if most of this is just visual contact.

Wood chippings/floor coverings
A popular type of floor covering is wood chippings that help absorb any spilled water and urine. Consideration must be given to the choice of wood chippings in order to avoid problems for your pet. Some wood chippings or sawdust come from wood that has been treated with anti-fungals and other preservatives that may be toxic to hamsters. Cedar, pine and cypress mulch contains the volatile oil, thujone, which can cause skin irritation as well as respiratory problems. Hamsters may suffer allergies such as hay fever, asthma and eczema, just like humans. Pinewood has aromatic oils that give it a pleasant 'woody' smell and this can mask dangerous toxic gases, such as ammonia from urine, that can build up in your hamster's cage if they are not cleaned out regularly or thoroughly. It is therefore recommended that you use wood chippings that are guaranteed to be safe for small animals.

Wood chippings are a very good absorbent, soaking up urine, water spills and juices from soft foods. This can result in a very low humidity within the cage and lead to increased moisture losses from the respiratory system and skin of the hamsters. Lower levels of fluids will need to be passed in the form of urine and that could increase the risks from bladder stone development.

Longhaired hamsters may have problems with the larger wood chippings that can get caught in their fur resulting in matting. In this case, opt for the finer wood chippings or wood based cat litter. However, do not use the fine sawdust as this can get into your hamster's eyes resulting in conjunctivitis.

Should either your hamster or a member of your household be allergic to wood chippings there are other alternatives, such as finely chopped straw and other dried plant materials that are now sold in compressed packs in pet shops. These make very good floor covering or bedding but are more expensive than wood chippings.

If you decide to use newspaper as flooring in the cage, ensure it is non-toxic. Companies who are environmentally friendly and use non-toxic print tend to advertise this fact in their newspaper, usually next to the recycled logo. And remember the ink print will come off onto your pet's coat, especially with white pets. Kitchen roll or blank newspaper, e.g. the paper used in fish and chip shops is a better option. However if you decide to use paper rather than another form of floor covering you will need to remove the soiled paper daily.

Bedding

The choice of bedding material is a subject of much discussion and debate. Based on experience and reports written on the subject, the best type of bedding is shredded paper or shredded cloth bedding. Some of the fluffy bedding materials, whilst being comfortable for the hamster, have been reported to cause health problems.

Bedding packed into their cheeks during nest building can lead to cheek pouch impaction or the bedding may be swallowed causing stomach blockages and constipation. It may also get wrap-ped around legs, cutting off blood circulation and, in some cases, resulting in gangrene and subsequent amputation of the limb.

Toilet paper or kitchen roll make excellent bedding. Given to your hamster in whole sheets they have great fun shredding it to make a nest.

Cage cleaning
Provided cages are cleaned out regularly by and large hamsters do not smell. Syrian hamsters tend to split their cages into a sleeping area, a place for storing food and a toilet area. Some even have a rubbish area where they place shells of monkey nuts or other unwanted food products. It is therefore easy to remove any soiled wood chippings from the toilet area in between full cage cleanouts. Some hamsters can even be trained to use a 'designer toilet' that can be removed each day and rinsed out. Alternatively, give them a large jam jar to use. Place it in the corner of the cage that they are using as their toilet area, placing some of the soiled wood chippings inside it to encourage your hamster to use it.

Cages ideally should be cleaned out once each week but make sure you return some of their food store afterwards as some hamsters can get quite anxious when their food hoard suddenly disappears. Uneaten fruit and vegetables should be removed on a daily basis to prevent them going mouldy and smelling.

Dwarf hamsters are not so methodical. Especially when keeping several together, the cages get soiled much faster than for solitary Syrians. The number you are keeping together will determine how often you clean them out, but at least once weekly is recommended. Campbells are prone to illnesses such as diabetes resulting in the consumption and urination of vast quantities of fluids. In this case their tanks will need to be cleaned out much more frequently.

When keeping more than one dwarf or Chinese hamster together, it is important that some of their bedding is returned each time after cage cleaning. The scents that they impart to the bedding ensure that they recognise the cage as belonging to them. If all the bedding and wood chippings that contain their own scents are removed, this can lead to them becoming disorientated and squabbles breaking out.

Cleaning products
Do not use human disinfectants in cages or tanks. Opt for ones specifically designed for use with animals. It is important to thoroughly clean out the cage weekly whilst removing uneaten food daily. Fungal spores and bacteria can multiply on bedding or uneaten food resulting in respiratory disease and digestive upsets - see Chapter 7 for more information.

Thorough and complete removal of all organic material is of more importance than the actual choice of disinfectant unless there is a specific disease problem involved. After cleaning, allow the cage and cage furniture to dry completely prior to replacing the inhabitants. This increases the quality of the cleaning process. Exposure of the cleaned cage and furniture to natural sunlight also acts as an extremely good natural disinfectant. When choosing a chemical disinfectant, some, such as Tamodine E, contain very good antiviral and anti-fungal properties.

When disinfecting a previously used cage for the arrival of a new animal or after an animal has died from a bacterial infection, use a strong pet disinfectant. Afterwards, leave the cage empty for a few days to allow the disinfectant to dry and the smell to abate before re-homing an animal into it. If a hamster has had 'wet tail' (see Chapter 7), it is recommended that the cage be washed in pet disinfectant and then left for 3 weeks for any traces of the infection to dissipate.

Do not spray air fresheners near cages nor use the plug in variety in rooms where hamster cages are situated, as hamsters are very sensitive to strong perfumes. Odour eliminators that truly neutralise smells are better than air fresheners that only hide smells by imparting an even stronger masking smell.

Chapter 3

Exercise, Handling and Grooming

What is the purpose of exercise?
There are many reasons for exercising apart from just keeping fit. These can be divided into four groups:

Psychological - in the wild, hamsters get a lot of exercise. Syrian hamsters may travel for up to 5 miles a night to find food and bedding. Dwarf hamsters can travel up to 1 mile. Therefore, when keeping such pets in captivity within the confines of a small cage, it is vital that they have a means of exercise to relieve boredom. Otherwise they can develop physical disorders.

Prevention of obesity - regular exercise can help prevent obesity that is sadly so commonplace with pet hamsters. Many foods and treats sold for hamsters contain honey or other fattening ingredients. It is therefore important that they are given an opportunity to work off some of these excess calories to prevent health problems later in life.

General health and muscle tone - as for humans, exercise helps maintain general health, cardiovascular function and muscle tone. Hamsters confined in too small a cage or with no means to exercise may develop poor muscle tone or even cage paralysis (see Chapter 7.)

Interaction between the owner and the pet - one of the primary reasons for keeping a pet is the pleasure derived from building a good relationship with them. There is no better way to encourage this bonding process than by just spending time playing with them.

Types of exercise

Wheels

Hamsters enjoy running in a wheel but it is vital that the wheel is big enough. Wheels that come with a newly purchased cage may be fine for a young hamster but might need to be discarded and replaced by a jumbo wheel as the hamster grows. Solid wheels are safer than ones with spokes that can trap feet and hair leading to injuries. If your hamster is using a wheel with spokes, weave a piece of cardboard in between the spokes to reduce such hazards. Also check that your hamster's fur does not get caught up in the centre rotating mechanism of the wheel. There are more expensive wheels available that are partly enclosed at the front which are not only safe since the hamster is unlikely to fall out but also tend to make less noise. The centre rotating mechanism is also much larger and almost impossible for the hamster to get its fur caught in it. The disadvantage with this type of wheel is that they tend to have a drainage slit which can be hazardous when several baby hamsters are trying to have a run at the same time as it is possible for one or more to catch their feet in them.

Periods of access to the wheel should be strictly limited for the very young and the very old hamsters. Constant access to the wheel for a very young hamster, no matter how much they seem to enjoy it, could lead to exhaustion while it could lead to a heart attack for an aged hamster.

Dwarf hamsters also enjoy running in their wheels. Be careful when using a freestanding wheel in their tank that they don't pull it over. They tend to have a habit of all wanting a go at the same time and often try to run in opposite directions! Some wheels can be attached to the side of the tank by a suction pad to prevent collapse. Dwarf hamsters kept as a colony should be provided with a tank roomy enough to fit an additional wheel.

Another variation is in the form of a plastic ball on a stand. The sides are absent enabling the hamsters to climb in and out. These allow several dwarf hamsters to exercise simultaneously with less chance of falling out.

Exercise Balls
Some hamsters relish running around inside a hamster ball. There are many different types, colours and sizes available that suit different breeds and sizes of hamster. Dwarf

hamsters do not have the body strength to move the standard size ball and therefore the mini ball has been designed for them. Monitor play in these balls carefully as they can easily get trapped under or between furniture. Uneven carpet or flooring can cause problems in the balls especially for the dwarfs with their lower body strength.

Hamsters should only be put in their exercise balls for short periods of time before returning them to their cages for rest and water. Never let your hamster run around upstairs near a staircase or near a fire. Be careful when there are other pets in the house as chasing a hamster in its ball can appear fun to a cat or dog but may be less than enjoyable for the hamster! If your hamster clearly does not enjoy going in an exercise ball and remains perfectly still and unable to move or falls asleep as soon as they have been put into it, do not force them. After all, this is supposed to be fun for them. Some hamsters do find exercise balls frightening, in which case they may just prefer to be handled or be allowed to roam, super-vised, around a safe area.

Ensure there are no poisonous plants near your hamster's cage or where they are playing. They are very curious animals and love to hoard anything they find. It is not unusual to discover that they have decided to take some fibres from the carpet or tassels from chair throws for their nest.

Knowing how much hamsters love escaping, make sure the ball is securely fastened. Some hamster balls that come in two halves can split open if the hamster hits a wall. Hamsters also have a way of figuring out how to escape by chewing the opening of the ball. For safety, tape round the centre join and across the doors. Whilst you will get through a lot tape during the lifetime of your hamster, it is a better option than seeing it making a bid for freedom as it dashes across your lounge floor or disappears behind your cooker. Do not block any of the air slits in the ball, however.

Other toys

Be careful when buying toys for your hamster. There are so many on the market that look fun from a human perspective but are cruel for the hamster. Where children are involved, it is important for them to realise that their hamster is a living creature and not just an inanimate toy for them to play with.

Dragsters look fun, but only go forwards and backwards or around in circles. Larger hamsters may have difficulty turning around in them in contrast to the hamster ball that is more manoeuvrable and roomy.

Try to vary the type of exercise you give your hamster. They love tubes to run through and obstacles to climb over. They are happy to explore and play with toilet rolls, small boxes, paper bags etc. There are also many plastic toys available in pet shops to choose from but ensure that any tube is large enough for them to get through easily. Ceramic versions that are less likely to be chewed than plastic can be handmade in pottery classes and add more individuality to your tank or cage. Dwarf hamsters love to set up complex and lengthy circuits in their homes crawling through tubes and climbing over obstacles like soldiers on an assault course.

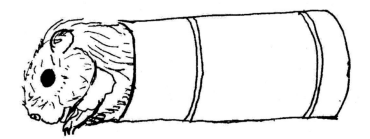

Play boxes are great fun for hamsters. Design and build your own to add originality. Use a large box, put wood chippings on the floor and a selection of toys: a wheel, tubes, apple branch, smooth pebbles, hidden treats etc. Don't forget to supervise your hamster when they are playing in their play box to prevent them from escaping.

Dwarf hamsters enjoy taking a dust bath. You can purchase 'Chinchilla dust' from pet shops. Place a small amount of this in a shallow dish for them to play in. The dish is best removed from the cage after play or it will be soiled.

Taming pets
This should begin as early in life as possible. When purchasing a hamster for a child, try to get one that has already been accustomed to handling. As for humans, it is those early experiences in life that set the patterns for behaviour later on in life.

Feeding time is a good time to tame a hamster. Offer it a small piece of food by hand or see if it will walk onto your hand to pick up some seeds. They will soon learn a daily routine and respond accordingly. Be warned, however, that hamsters are short sighted and rely heavily on sense of smell so accidental bites often occur because a finger or hand is mistaken for food. This is not true aggression, however. Do not be tempted to put your finger through the cage bars as hamsters can be extremely fast at biting them.

These little creatures also develop their own routines that are fascinating to watch. Once you get to know these routines, you can plan playtime and feeding around them. Alternatively, it is possible to train them to fit in with your routine so that they rise earlier in the evening, which is ideal if the hamster belongs to a child.

Alfie would never come out in his ball until he had climbed to the top of his cage and had a wash and brush up in a house situated on the third floor. Only after this would he climb back down and wait by the doorway in his cage to be let out for a run around.

Cassie had equally strange habits. As soon as she realised she was about to be let out of her cage for a run around in her ball she would rush off and quickly pack her cheek pouches with stored food. She would then stand beside the doorway in her cage to indicate that she was ready to go for a run.

Handling

Warning: Human 'cold' viruses and bacteria can infect hamsters resulting in severe disease. Therefore, avoid allowing people with colds and flu to handle your hamster.

Due to their poor eyesight, take care when handling hamsters. In the wild attacks on hamsters often come from above. Therefore they can react with fear and aggression when they sense a hand coming down on them, as they will assume it is a predator. This is one of the reasons why hamsters get stressed when being picked up. If your hamster is especially timid and nervous about being picked up, try to win their confidence by coaxing them onto your hand. Alternatively use a soft toothbrush to gently stroke them. Continue stroking them even if they initially try to bite the toothbrush and in time they will realise that the stroking does not represent a threat and you should be able to pick them up.

Always talk to your hamster before you try to pick it up. After a while they will recognise your voice and will feel more at ease with you.

Syrian hamsters should be scooped up from underneath or picked up from above, although if you are doing this be careful not to squeeze them too much. Scruffing refers to lifting and holding the hamster by the skin along the back of the neck and is not recommended for routinely picking up your hamster. Anyone who has tried this will know how difficult it is. If they are scruffed too tightly the pressure on their head can lead to a prolapsed eye. The only time scruffing should be done is for inspection of teeth or claws. Hamsters have a huge amount of loose skin around their head and necks that all needs to be gathered up and the hamster needs to be supported well while this is being done.

Hamsters like to keep on the move. Only the very placid ones will sit quietly in your hand. More often than not, this will be a male rather than female. They have poor perception of depth so never leave them unattended on tables or other high objects. They will willingly walk over the edge resulting in injuries or death. Since hamsters have extremely poor sight, quick or jerky movements startle them so stroking and handling should be smooth and confident.

Dwarf hamsters are very fast, especially Roborovski hamsters and can be quite difficult to handle. Attempt to catch them in cupped hands; alternatively use a toy tube or plastic cup to scoop them up. In many ways Roborovski hamsters are better for children to watch rather than to play with because they are so quick. They are great fun and entertaining to observe, especially when there are several living together in a tank.

46

One idea for a child who is initially nervous of handling their hamster and afraid that it might escape, is for them to sit fully clothed in a dry bath (with the plug in) along with their hamster. They can then play and gain more confidence with their hamster without fear of it running off. There is plenty of room to move around but no opportunity for escape or accidental falls resulting in broken limbs.

Campbells are very territorial but they are often more placid once they are out of their cage. Colonies normally have a dominant female who will try to prevent you from picking up other hamsters. If any hamster in the colony is going to bite, it will probably be her. Having identified the dominant female, try to isolate her in some way to allow you to gain access to the other hamsters. The best method to pick them up is to gently put your hand flat on top of them and then scoop them up or cup them from both sides.

Winter Whites are relatively easy to handle and can be picked up the same way as Campbells.

Chinese hamsters can also be handled relatively easily once they have been tamed. They are extremely timid to begin with and try to find places to hide in their cage. Although they move quite quickly, they are easy to handle once caught. They use their claws and tails to hold onto people. They seldom bite and it is possible to tame them, which makes them a good pet.

Chinese hamsters are renowned for clinging onto things and will happily fall asleep clinging upside down to your finger. However, Noodles goes one stage further. When his owner gets him out of his cage he likes to gather a few strands of her hair in his paws, wraps himself round them and falls asleep!

Sounds
Some hamsters are more vocal than others. Occasionally they snore or squeak as though they are chatting. If you disturb them while they are sleeping, they tend to grind their teeth to warn you off. When startled, they might cry out loudly. When keeping a colony of dwarf hamsters or pairs of Chinese or Winter Whites, it is worth investigating if you hear any unusual sounds. They may just be playing but they could also be fighting with one hamster in distress or injured. Winter Whites and Campbells are very vocal and often squeal at each other if one wants to get its own way.

48

Lost pets

It is easy to lose a pet as small and fast as a hamster. This is all the more so if the room is full of nooks and crannies so it is important to make your room hamster proof before buying your pet. If you do find your pet has escaped, the first rule is DO NOT PANIC - your pet is probably terrified at being alone in the big wide world and panicking will only cause more distress for all concerned. A logical and calm approach to a search and rescue mission is most likely to lead to a successful conclusion.

Start by checking the room where the cage is situated after first rechecking the cage itself for the escapee. Ensure that any other free roaming pets are shut out of the room while you check behind and under furniture. Restrict the number of people in the room looking for your pet to avoid excessive noise and alarm and to reduce the chances of the hamster being trodden under well-meaning feet! Gently move any items out of the way, listening for any telltale signs of their presence. It is surprising what small spaces they can get into so explore every possibility.

Listen carefully because your hamster may start crying or squealing when they are afraid or you may hear the scrabbling of their feet as they move around, making them easier to locate. Large pieces of foods such as carrots or cucumber may be left out overnight in several rooms after a hamster escape. By checking whether the food gets eaten, you will at least identify which room the hamster is in. Once you have identified the room, try to block up additional means of escape so there is only one exit point.

Try to coax or gently ease them out of their hiding place with a favourite treat. Be careful with handling your pet at this time, as it is likely to be very traumatised from its ordeal and may bite out of fear. Alternatively, try to entice the lost hamster into a container. Put wood chippings and bedding from their own cage that still has their own scent along with some of their favourite foods into the bottom of a bucket and make a stairway up to the top of the bucket by stacking books. Ensure that each step is not too high for them to climb. Results from this procedure may take some time, especially if your hamster decides not to stir until nightfall. Leave the door of the room closed overnight and hopefully they will follow the food trail and drop into the bucket and not be able to get out.

For Russian and Chinese hamsters on the run, it is possible to use a humane mousetrap. Put their favourite food into the trap and leave it along the edge of the skirting board. Once they have entered the chamber where the food is stored they will find themselves trapped as the door closes behind them. When using this type of trap, check it regularly for the return of your hamster and then rapidly return them to the familiar surroundings of their cage for rest, food and drink.

If you are unsure where your hamster is, do not start blocking up holes indiscriminately as you may just trap your hamster. Ensure that all cables are protected, as they love chewing through these. If you do know which room your hamster is in, restrict access of other pets to the area as they may well frighten it further, or worse still, catch it.

Once you have finally recovered your pet, return it to its cage as soon as possible and leave it in peace in order to recover from its ordeal.

Never give up hope in finding a lost hamster. They can survive long periods of time outside of their cage. If you find your hamster and it appears dead, remember that it might just have gone into hibernation. Check patiently for even the slightest signs of life such as breathing or tiny movements. Warm it gently in your hands to see if it will revive or replace it in its cage situated in a warm airing cupboard. If there is still no movement, ask your vet to check to see for vital signs by listening with a stethoscope for a heartbeat. Hibernating hamsters can appear stiff and cold and it is vital they are not accidentally buried because the owner believes them to be dead.

Nicholas, the Syrian hamster, was in his cage in the lounge. His owner decided to go upstairs to watch T.V. Unbeknown to her the cage door had accidentally been left open. Tempted by the idea of freedom, Nicholas decided to venture out of his cage and go looking for his owner. Guided by her laughter he climbed the flight of stairs and sat himself down on the floor next to her!

Ways of preventing an escape
There are several causes for escapes. Sometimes this can happen when hamsters are being handled or if their cage door

has been left open or not securely fastened. A momentary lapse of concentration or a distraction when handling a hamster can result in a lot of time being spent recapturing them. Get into the habit of using the same cage door when removing and replacing the hamster. This avoids the common mistake of having safely closed the door when replacing the hamster only to have forgotten that the door through which it was removed had been left open.

Whilst there are many unforeseen circumstances, some precautions can be taken. When a child is handling a hamster, close the door to the room and restrict access by cats and dogs. Should the hamster escape, this ensures easier location. Always double check that the cage door has been securely fastened after returning the hamster to its nest. It only takes a split second for your pet to escape if the door has been left open.

Wire cages are usually attached to their bases by two clips that can easily be lost or broken. Replacements can be obtained from your pet shop. Alternatively, repairs can be carried out at home by making a hole in the side of the cage and threading a piece of wire through to secure the top to the base. Holes are fashioned by melting the plastic with a hot skewer. Never use string for such a repair, as hamsters will just chew their way to freedom!

Glass tanks often used for dwarf hamsters tend to have a top opening covered by a mesh screen. Clips at all four corners normally secure these lids but constant vibration from hamsters during play can loosen and unlock these clips. Taping down one or two corners of the tank to secure them reduces this risk.

To ensure the joins of tubular structures are secure, any loose sections can be taped together but do not tape over ventilation slits.

Hamsters that continually chew at the bars may open side doors of cages. Their body weight and persistent vibration on the door can sometimes open it. To avoid this happening, the door can be secured by a piece of wire, ensuring that the cut ends of the wire are outside the cage to prevent injury. Alternatively, position the cage with the door flush against the wall and move the water bottle to the other side of the cage, if necessary. If the hamster were able to open the door they would not have the body strength to push the cage far enough away from the wall to get free.

It is worth taking time to check your pet's cage regularly for any damage that may lead to an escape.

I decided to move Scud, one of my baby hamsters, into a cage on his own because his brothers were picking on him. The only one available was a glass tank which, due to lack of space, I placed on the floor under a table. The following morning Scud had escaped, the mesh top to the cage having been pushed to one side. I tracked down a very frightened hamster behind a piece of furniture and returned him to his cage, taping the mesh top down to prevent any future escape, although I couldn't understand how such a small hamster could remove such a heavy lid. Later I discovered Jasper, my house bunny, sitting next to Scud's cage and playing with the mesh top. Then I realised that she had in fact orchestrated the escape!

Grooming

Haircare

Most hamsters are covered with beautiful soft short hair that needs little if any specific care. Some of the exotic breeds have been selected to have long hair. This does make them very pretty but remember that these varieties do not exist in

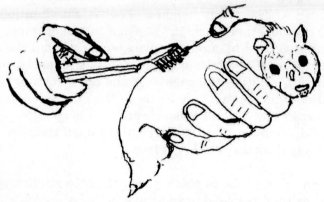

the wild and do have their disadvantages. They need to be combed regularly to avoid the hair getting matted or knotted. If the hair is badly matted, it is best to trim it short. Do not worry too much about the cosmetic effect, as it will always re-grow later. Hamster brushes are available in the pet shops, or alternatively you can use an old toothbrush. Start grooming your hamster when it is young to get it used to the idea of being brushed.

Nails

As for our own fingertips, all hamster toes should have a nail. The nail grows from the skin covering the tip of the toe and is important for gripping onto climbing surfaces and digging. The nail has a pink blood vessel in its centre which can usually be seen from the outside and which extends about half to three-quarters the length of the nail. This blood vessel will bleed profusely if it is cut. The vein is also accompanied by a sensitive nerve, which hurts if it is pinched. Most young hamsters should not need to have their nails cut as they will either chew them to keep them short or wear them down during natural wear and tear. However, due to age, severe dental disease or obesity, nails may grow too long and require regular trimming. Shorter trimmed nails are less likely to get caught up in bedding or the bars of the cage bars leading to injuries. You may wish to take your hamster to your vet to have the nails trimmed but it is possible to attempt this at home. Firstly provide yourself with a set of sharp small nail clippers from the pet shop. The human guillotine-style nail clippers also work well. The safest way of doing this is to hold the hamster by the scruff, taking care to handle them carefully to avoid damaging their eyes. It is advisable to have an assistant to steady the leg during the nail clipping. The nails can be safely clipped as shown in the diagram, making sure to always leave a few millimetres between the point of clipping and the visible tip of the vein. Slightly close the blades first where you plan to clip to check if you are cutting the nail too short. If the animal suddenly withdraws its leg, release the clipper blades and reposition them closer to the tip of the nail. Keep repeating this test until the animal displays no pain before actually clipping the nail. The whole process gets much easier and faster with time and experience.

Should you accidentally cut the nail too short, or if your hamster ever accidentally injures its nail causing bleeding, apply firm pressure to the bleeding point with some dry cotton wool for a few minutes until the bleeding stops. Alternatively, apply ferric chloride or silver nitrate if you have some.

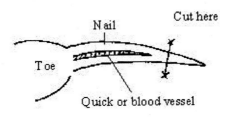

Chapter 4

Diet

Feeding the correct diet is extremely important to help maintain good mental and physical health for your hamster. As for humans, a hamster diet should include proteins, carbohydrates, fats, vitamins and minerals. In addition clean water must be available at all times. However, as well as the nutritional breakdown of the foods, there are several other factors to take into account when selecting the type and method of feeding for your hamsters.

In the wild, hamsters survive on a diet of mostly grasses, seeds and small insects. In captivity this is somewhat different but it is worth trying to keep the foods offered as close as possible to the wild diet. The presence of a hidden food hoard is as important psychologically for the pet hamster as it is for its wild cousins, so this natural habit should be encouraged.

Food for health

Hamster mixes of varying composition can be purchased from pet shops and grocery stores. These are ready mixes that contain a mixture of pellets, seeds and nuts. Your pet will sort through them, taking just the items they prefer. It is worth alternating the source of these mixes to give your pet some variety and novelty in its food. Dwarf hamsters in particular enjoy eating mixed birdseed, which can be added to their food. They also need to take in more protein than Syrians, which can be given in the form of small pieces of boiled egg or cheese.

A small quantity of fresh food should be given on a daily basis. Fruits and vegetables should be washed thoroughly before giving them to your pet to remove any covering of pesticides or other chemicals that could make your pet ill. Examples of suitable foods with their nutritional charact-eristics are given in Appendix I. Vary the fresh foods given and ensure any uneaten fresh foods are removed each day to prevent decaying foods being eaten or smelling.

Although ideal when taken from your own garden, be careful when offering wild plants e.g. dandelion, chickweed, that have been picked from the roadside because contamination from exhaust fumes, pesticides

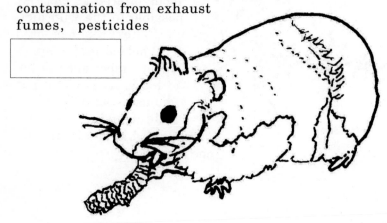

and weed killers may render them toxic. Some pesticides can be removed by washing the plant in an acidic medium, e.g. vinegar. Use one table-spoon of vinegar to a bowl of water as a wash solution. Once you have washed the food in this mixture, thoroughly rinse with water after-wards before giving to your pet.

If your pet is recovering from an illness or surgery, food supplements can be given in the form of vitamin drops or powder. These can be purchased from your veterinary surgery or pet shop and added to the drinking water or food.

Feeding your hamster dandelion leaves as a treat can help prevent bladder stones by increasing urine production to dilute urine crystals and flush the bladder.

Food for boredom/play
In the wild, hamsters travel miles each day in their quest for food resulting in additional benefits of both mental and physical stimulation. There are a number of commercial food products available, such as wooden sticks coated with nuts and seeds, which help alleviate boredom for pet hamsters. These sticks encourage your pet to work hard to release the food by chewing and also help maintain good dental wear. However, the downside is that these foods are usually adhered to the stick with honey that promotes tooth decay. It is recommended that these sticks be given only as treats and not as the main part of their diet. Another treat that you can give is millet sprays. These are not only nutritious but also fun to eat.

Although not strictly carnivorous, hamsters can be provided with cooked bones from which to nibble small pieces of meat. This is nutritionally sound as well as keeping the incisor teeth in good condition. The nibbling process keeps the hamsters active and reduces the monotony from a caged existence.

There are other ways to make feeding time fun. Place treats inside tubes or a feeding ball so the hamsters have work out how to get to it. Alternatively you could suspend a treat from a piece of string tied to the bars or roof of their cage.

'Scatter Feeding' mimics the natural method of questing for food. Food pieces are scattered and hidden in the floor covering material. The natural instinct of hamsters is to forage for this food. As well as greatly relieving boredom, this will increase the levels of exercise taken and improve general fitness. In addition, these natural behaviours are a joy to watch.

Food for interaction
The primary purpose for any owner keeping a pet should be the pleasure of interaction. Feeding times are ideal opportunities for this form of play and can result in a strengthening of the bond between pet and owner. Nuts and other small treats, such as sultanas or raisins, can be fed through the bars of the cage. Hamsters love to pack their cheek pouches full with nuts or to store them away in their nests. They will easily get into a routine where they will come and wait for you to feed them.

> *A word of warning!! Marmaduke loves taking nuts through the bars of his cage and packing them in his cheeks before sorting through them and adding them to his hoard. One day, I half pushed a walnut through the bars and left him to work out how to get it through completely. I curiously watched him as he snapped the walnut in half and without warning a piece of it catapulted out of his cage and went straight in my eye!*

When feeding nuts, ensure they are good quality. Do not feed the bulk peanuts often sold for bird food unless the pet shop can guarantee they are safe for hamsters. Never give your pet any nut that looks mouldy as these can be contaminated with a fungus called aspergillus that is very toxic for hamsters. Salted or dry roasted nuts are also not advisable.

Beware of pet chocolate products. Although these do not contain any real chocolate and are just coloured types of fat, they can cause an impaction in hamster cheek pouches. When hamsters fill their cheek pouches with sweets or other sticky foods but do not empty them immediately, the sweets may melt and adhere to the lining of the cheek pouches. This can create problems emptying the pouches and lead to infections.

Do not feed 'human' treat foods such as biscuits or sweets to hamsters. These often have high sugar contents and can damage teeth. Never give real chocolate to a hamster. A chemical in chocolate called theobromine is highly toxic to hamsters. Bread and baby foods are safe to give during hamster pregnancy, to baby hamsters or during convalescence and old age. The disadvantage of using them apart from these times on a regular basis is that no chewing is required to eat them and thus the teeth may become overgrown. Avoid feeding citrus fruits, as these are too acidic for hamsters.

> **Warning**: *Branches from trees that produce stoned fruit such as plums or peaches may be toxic. Chocolate is also toxic for hamsters. Certain decorative garden plants and trees are also extremely toxic such as laurel, laburnum, yew and rhododendron.*

Very small quantities of fresh food should be given on a daily basis, e.g. a slice of apple, a French bean, small broccoli floret. Corn on the cob is also a great favourite with hamsters. Introduce any new foods gradually, alternating as much as possible to ensure variety and to maintain a well balanced diet. Lettuce may cause diarrhoea due to its high water content and is best avoided.

On average, adult Syrian hamsters consume 5.5 - 7g of food daily. Therefore ensure sufficient staple foods supplies are available.

> **Tip**: *Purchase sweet corn when it is in season and readily available. Cut each cob into four or five pieces and freeze. It is then easy to take one piece out a week and defrost it for your hamster. They can also eat the outer leaves so long as these are fresh and not dried up.*

Special diets

Dealing with Diabetes
Diabetes mellitus refers to a disease state resulting from excessively high blood and urine sugar levels. Campbells seem particularly prone to developing diabetes. Some affected individuals die prematurely whilst others survive and in effect cure themselves. Affected hamsters drink vast quantities of water.

Your vet should examine any hamster suspected of having diabetes. A blood or urine test can be used to confirm the disease. As an initial screening test at home, a urine glucose test kit called Diastix can be purchased from your chemist, which will enable you to test hamster's urine at home. A urine sample can be obtained by placing your hamster into a carry case with no bedding and waiting for them to urinate. The urine can then easily be poured into a sample bottle for testing.

For colony hamsters, it is necessary to test each hamster individually, with thorough washing and drying of the carry case between each one. It is vital that any hamsters identified as having high urine glucose by these tests are examined by your veterinary surgeon before accepting a diagnosis of diabetes. Other factors such as stress, pregnancy or diets high in sugars can also cause glucose to be present in urine and thus lead to a false positive diagnosis with potentially disastrous consequences.

As well as any medical treatment (see Chapter 7), the following dietary factors are important:

Obesity plays a major role in the development of diabetes. Ensure your hamster receives a well balanced diet that prevents obesity and allow plenty of exercise. Hide food in their cage to encourage foraging to find it. This mimics the natural situation where wild hamsters travel long distances each night to collect their food.

It is very important to keep blood sugar levels of affected animals balanced. Avoid foods that release sugars quickly in the body, e.g. refined foods, sweets, dried fruit and sugary foods and replace them with foods that contain slow releasing carbohydrates plus some protein e.g. nuts with fruit. Avoid giving your hamster 'treats' that are available in the pet shops as these often contain high levels of sugar, sometimes in the form of honey. All vegetables contain fibre that delays absorption of sugars from the intestine during digestion and thus helps to smooth out blood sugar levels.

Flossie and Katie were two Campbells, Flossie being the smallest in the litter. Their water consumption was extremely high and at the age of only 4 months Katie died. The rest of the extended family also died prematurely with suspected diabetes. Flossie, however, went on to live until she was 18 months old and died from a tumour. During her life, her water consumption gradually reduced and she ate small amounts of food on and off all day long. Although she was slightly 'chubby' due to her constant picking at food, she did appear to cure herself of diabetes.

In addition to a well balanced diet for your diabetic hamster, the following vitamins and minerals are needed. If you are unable to provide these in the diet a vitamin and mineral supplement may be needed. These can be purchased in the form of drops or powder that can be added to the water or food.

Chromium
Vitamin C
Essential Fatty Acids
Vitamin E
Magnesium
Manganese
Zinc
B Vitamins

Teeth problems/old age

Providing your pet with the correct diet and enough items to chew during its life should help ensure teeth are in good condition in old age. However, constant chewing on cage bars or illness can damage teeth and cause unequal growth. Also, some hamsters are born with congenital dental problems. In these situations, it may be necessary to have the teeth clipped regularly by your vet.

A nine-year-old boy came back to the pet shop after two months of caring for his new hamster, to collect his Care Certificate. This Certificate is given after health inspection of the hamster and correct answers to certain questions put to the owner - showing responsible pet ownership. On this occasion, however, the hamster felt very light, not its correct weight at all. The young boy was very pleased with his new pet and said that his hamster licked hin a great deal and never bit him! You' ve guessed it - there was not a tooth in the hamster's mouth, and would never be, having been born with gums alone. The boy burst into tears when told that specialist care would be needed. Another hamster was given to him and another relationship developed. Our toothless hamster in fact had a very long life - living mainly on baby food.

If your hamster is having difficulty eating due to dental problems despite regular veterinary attention, it may be necessary to provide softer foods to avoid malnutrition or starvation. Discuss this carefully with your vet before altering the diet, as you may need to continue this feeding for the duration of the hamster's life. Harder food such as dog biscuits should still be offered to encourage chewing.

Suggested soft diets include:

Sprouted soaked seeds and beans
Standard hamster food ground up in a blender and mixed with water
Pureed Fruit
Homemade vegetable soup (made from liquidised vegetables. Do not add seasoning.)
Ground almonds soaked in water
Baby rice or rusks in either water or milk*
Vegetable-based baby food
Scrambled egg (only give once a week)
Bread in milk*

* Try to avoid using too much milk as it may lead to digestive upsets or diarrhoea. Specialised cat milk may be better because the lactose (milk sugar) has been pre-digested to improve digestibility. It also contains about twice the energy of normal milk.

> **Tip**: *When making vegetable soup for your pet, freeze it down into an ice cube tray. This allows the removal of one cube at a time and thus cuts down on waste.*

It might also be necessary to supplement your hamster's diet with vitamin drops such as S.A. VITS (Vitamins A and C) or ACE-HIGH (Vitamins A, B, C and E). Details of these and other dietary supplements can be found in Chapter 8.

Treats
The following foods can be given weekly in very small amounts as treats:

Hard-boiled egg
Cheese
Fish
Chicken
Lamb
Mealworms
Toast
Dog biscuits

Hamsters also love porridge, rice pudding, yoghurt and fromage frais. These are all a good source of calcium especially for pregnant or nursing females and hamsters under 4 months old. However, these should be given in moderation.

Never feed your hamster bacon, spicy or salty food. In the wild hamsters eat small insects, and in captivity they can be given mealworms. If you wish to give these occasionally and do not wish to handle the mealworm, use tweezers to feed them to your hamster.

Importance of vitamins and minerals

Hamsters need a balanced diet to maintain their health just like humans. Although only small amounts of vitamins and minerals are required, a deficiency of any of these can lead to disease. Some of the important vitamins and minerals with their deficiency signs are given below whilst a guide to dietary sources are given in Appendix I at the end of the book.

Vitamin A is very important for the immune system, healthy skin, and night vision and is an antioxidant to delay ageing signs.

Deficiency Signs: Frequent colds or infection, dry flaky skin, diarrhoea.

B Vitamins are essential for energy production, brain function, healthy hair, nails, eyes and skin. B Vitamins also help to balance blood sugar and lower cholesterol levels and are involved in digestion. Vitamin B calms the nerves and can be given to help a nervous or stressed hamster. Some conditions are associated with stress, e.g. 'wet tail'; a Vitamin B supplement can be used to help prevent this. Some people also believe that diabetes in Campbells can be triggered by stress. Ensure that sufficient foods containing Vitamin B are provided.

Deficiency signs: Constipation, rapid heartbeat, cataracts, dull or oily hair, eczema or dermatitis, diarrhoea, anxiety.

Vitamin C is a powerful antioxidant and strengthens the immune system. Vitamin C is essential for the formation of collagen, which is important for the production of bones, joints and skin. Vitamin C is important for adrenal gland function and aids in the production of anti-stress hormones.

Deficiency signs: Lack of energy, poor wound healing, easy bruising, frequent infections.

Calcium is vital for the formation of strong bones and teeth. *Deficiency signs*: Tooth decay, susceptibility to fractures, muscle cramps or tremors, joint pain or arthritis. Do not overfeed with Sunflower seeds, as these are particularly low in calcium and should never form a major part of the diet.

Chromium forms part of the glucose tolerance factor, which helps to balance blood sugar.

Deficiency signs: Excessive or cold sweats, need for frequent meals, excessive sleep or drowsiness, excessive thirst.

Vitamin D is required for the absorption and utilisation of calcium and phosphorus by the intestinal tract. It protects against brittle bones that are easily fractured, muscle weakness and is involved in regulation of the heartbeat.

Deficiency signs: Loss of appetite, diarrhoea, hair loss, weight loss and a high frequency of broken bones.

Vitamin E is an antioxidant; it improves circulation, is necessary for tissue repair, promotes normal blood clotting and maintains healthy nerves and muscles. It also helps to maintain healthy skin and hair.

Deficiency signs: Easy bruising, slow wound healing.

Essential fatty acids are needed for the cardiovascular and nervous system, healthy skin and hormone production. A good balance for Essential Fatty Acids is to mix Sunflower, Sesame, Pumpkinseeds and Linseeds together.

Deficiency signs: Inflammatory problems like arthritis, blood sugar problems or diabetes, excessive thirst, infertility, poor wound healing.

Folic Acid is critical during pregnancy for the development of the brain and nerves. Needed for energy production and the formation of red blood cells, it strengthens immunity and is involved in protein metabolism.

Deficiency signs: Lack of energy, poor appetite and stomach pains.

Vitamin K is essential for blood clotting and for bone formation and repair.

Deficiency signs: Abnormal and/or internal bleeding.

Iron is involved in the production of haemoglobin and myoglobin (the form of haemoglobin found in muscle tissue) and the oxygenation of red blood cells. Iron is also important for a healthy immune system and for energy production.

Deficiency signs: Fragile bones, hair loss, anaemia and digestive disturbances.

Magnesium is important for energy production and the absorption of calcium.

Deficiency signs: Muscle tremors or spasms, muscle weakness, constipation, fits or convulsions, hyperactivity and lack of appetite.

Manganese is used in energy production and is required for normal bone, cartilage, tissue and nerve growth.

Deficiency signs: Muscle twitches, poor sense of balance, fits, convulsions and joint pain.

Potassium enables nutrients to move into cells and waste products to move out of cells. It helps in blood sugar balance, is involved in metabolism, maintains heart function and promotes healthy nerves and muscles.

Deficiency signs: Diarrhoea and vomiting.

Selenium is an antioxidant and stimulates the immune system. It is needed for metabolism and promotes a healthy heart.

Deficiency signs: Cataracts and frequent infections.

Zinc is very important for digestion and the immune system. It also helps the body cope with stress and promotes a healthy nervous system and brain.

Deficiency signs: Frequent infections and loss of appetite.

Water

Why give it?
Water is essential to life. A hamster's body comprises 60-70% water. Water ensures the correct function of all cells and organs. Without water, death will occur over a relatively short period of time and certainly within a few days. It is vital that your pet does not even get slightly dehydrated as

this can lead to subsequent problems such as kidney failure. Ensure a fresh clean supply of water is always available.

Ways to offer water

Water is best provided in a bottle. Dishes of water may get knocked over or filled with wood chippings or food. They can be extremely dangerous for baby hamsters who may fall in and drown. Where there are babies in a tank/cage ensure they can reach the water bottle. Either place an upturned dish by the water bottle for them to climb up to reach it or build up the wood chippings in that area. One word of warning is that if the upturned dish is not completely flat against the base of the cage, it is possible for a baby to push its way underneath and get crushed.

Make sure water bottles are situated well away from the bed in case of leakage. They are best positioned high so that the hamster has to stand up to drink. If the bottle ever accidentally gets drained, remember to immediately remove all the soggy bedding. The bottle should be emptied and cleaned daily before refilling with clean cold water.

When keeping Campbells, it is important that the colony has sufficient water reserves, especially if some members are diabetic. In extreme circumstances of insufficient water supply, the weakest in the colony may be killed to ensure the survival of the majority.

Should your pet clearly be getting dehydrated, for example because of illness or over-heating, water can be dropped directly into the mouth. Use either a dropper bottle or syringe (without the needle). Alternatively, oral rehydration powders (electrolyte mixes) may be added to the drinking water.

Follow the instructions given on the packet and refrigerate any that is not used immediately. Your vet can advise you on this and details of electrolyte mixes are given in Chapter 8.

Other uses of water

In some situations where it is not possible to directly medicate your hamster, then the drug may be added to the drinking water. Antibiotics are often administered in this fashion. Should the medication be unpalatable and it is clear that your pet is avoiding drinking it, add a few grains of sugar or a dash of children's blackcurrant juice to the water bottle to mask the medication and encourage drinking.

Water as a means of identifying illness

Excessive water consumption can highlight the start of a medical problem and should always prompt you to take your hamster to your veterinary surgeon for a full examination.

An increase in water consumption can signal the start of diabetes or kidney problems. Occasionally, increased drinking may result from the development of a cancer somewhere in the body.

During pregnancy and while producing milk soon after giving birth, a hamster will increase her water intake. This is perfectly natural and consumption will return to normal levels once the litter has been weaned.

Chapter 5

Breeding

This chapter provides general information on the breeding of hamsters and also highlights where differences apply between the different breeds. Serious consideration should be given to your motivation before considering breeding from your hamsters for several reasons.

The mating process itself can be dangerous with either or both parties involved getting seriously injured. It is important to remember that there is no direct benefit to the adults involved from the mating or breeding process and that breeding should only be undertaken if the owner specifically wishes for babies.

Some Syrian hamster litters may number 12 or more babies so plans need to be made in advance for re-homing them. Whereas Campbells or Roborovski hamsters would only require two very large tanks/cages depending on the number of each sex, Syrian hamsters will each require a separate cage. Winter Whites and Chinese hamsters can be kept in pairs of either the same or different sex but, even then, they will need to be separated if they fight.

Furthermore, there are plenty of unwanted animals already in this world. Should you just wish to increase your household number of hamsters, a trip to the local pet rescue centre is a much better idea.

Should there be a vicious streak in either parent, if the female is skittish or if there is any hereditary illness such as diabetes, then it is unwise to breed as these characteristics are hereditary and may be passed onto the babies.

However, so long as all these issues have been considered and you still feel that it is appropriate to begin a breeding programme, then the following information should be of assistance. Breeding hamsters can be an absorbing and fascinating hobby as well as being highly educational for children.

Syrian hamsters

Although the females are fertile from 6 weeks onwards, it is best to wait until they are at least 12 weeks to begin breeding. Syrian hamsters are solitary creatures so the mating itself can be fraught with difficulties. Usually the female comes into season every 4 days. However, before putting her with a male, it is important to ascertain which is the 4th day because on this day she will be receptive to the male whereas, on the other days of her cycle, she can be extremely aggressive. Females tend to have a distinctive odour around the time of coming into season.

Place the female on the top of the male's cage and let them sniff each other through the bars. Once the female has been there for a few minutes, rub your finger gently along her back. This mimics the sensations from being mounted by the male. If she is in season she will flatten her body out and raise her tail. Whilst this test is not 100% fool proof, it is a good guide. If she shows no interest at all, try again later that same evening and again the following evening. Should she respond positively, place her in 'neutral territory' such as a washing up bowl or a dry bath (with the plug in). Never put the male into the female's cage, as this is likely to provoke an attack. Monitor them very closely and have a jar or other container at hand that you can use to separate them should they start fighting. Never leave them unattended together for any reason. Allow the male to mate repeatedly with the female for up to 20 minutes. When the female becomes restless, it is time to separate them. After a successful mating, both the male and female tend to wash themselves.

A test mating to check for pregnancy can be performed 4 days later at the time that the non-pregnant female would be in season again. Go through the same procedure as before but be extra vigilant when putting them together as the female is likely to be very aggressive if she is pregnant. This test is not a total guarantee of pregnancy as conception can sometimes be followed by resorption of the embryos a few days later. In these cases, the cycle will have changed and you should be careful when next trying to mate them as the female will be a day or two late coming into season.

When both hamsters are sexually inexperienced, it might take a number of mating processes before being successful so be prepared to keep repeating the procedure every 4th day until conception occurs. Also try mating them at different times in the evening and night as the female is in season for a matter of only a few hours.

Gestation lasts 16-18 days for Syrian hamsters. About a week before giving birth, the female may increase the amount of water she is drinking. She also starts to prepare her nest, moving it from one position to another and sorting through food. Clean her cage thoroughly around this time, as you will not be able to clean her out until about 2 weeks after the birth of her litter. Ensure she has sufficient bedding. It is important for her to feel comfortable around the birthing time. Any sudden changes to her surroundings can be stressful and should be avoided. After the birth, just remove any soiled wood chippings as necessary but leave the nest untouched.

Physical signs of pregnancy may be hard to detect. Pregnant Syrians tend to carry their young more on their hips and when stretching up the bars, the 'bulge' will remain. You will not always detect much change in the female's size if she is pregnant with a small litter, e.g. less than 8. The average litter size is 10-12 babies.

Increasing dietary protein and calcium by supplementing with foods such as milk products, egg or cheese on the days leading up to the birth ensures that the mother and her unborn babies are well nourished. However, avoid overfeeding as the babies may grow too big and compromise a safe delivery. Just prior to the birth, remove the wheel and any bowls or toys. Babies are very vulnerable in the early stages and it is quite possible for them to get trapped under wheels or bowls.

The birthing itself is normally straightforward and usually happens at night. She will clean each baby as it is born. Do not disturb her during the birth or attempt to touch her babies soon afterwards. The babies are born completely bald and with their eyes closed. As their skin is quite transparent, it is possible to see milk in their stomachs once they have been fed. A solid sided cage is safer for breeding hamsters to avoid babies being pushed through the bars.

It is not unusual for the female to both kill and eat her young or to chew off parts of their bodies. This holds for all types of hamsters and may result from the female being frightened, insufficient food or water supplies or because a baby is ill. When keeping a colony of Campbells or Roborovski hamsters, ensure the tank is large enough. If they feel they are running out of room, this might prompt cannibalism. Sometimes there is no logical explanation for cannibalism. It is unlikely that newborn babies would survive without their mother so it is best to avoid separating the mother from the litter. Equally, fostering the litter to another hamster is rarely successful but is perhaps worth trying in an emergency. It is worth remembering that mother hamsters can safely pick up and carry their litters in their cheek pouches without doing them any harm. Witnessing this is not evidence of any tendency towards cannibalism.

Occasionally an over zealous female will clean her young too much when they are newborn. This can result in the limbs of her babies being accidentally bitten off. In this case, discuss the situation with your veterinary surgeon. Unless there are major limb abnormalities, many such amputees are able to live a normal life.

During the first week after birth, the ears, fingers and toes of the babies become clear. A fluffy covering on the skin will appear and it is possible to get an indication of any banding or colouring at this stage. If their eyes can be seen through their eyelids as black dots, then the eyes will be black. If you cannot see their eyes, then they will have pink eyes that tend to darken as they age.

As the babies approach one week old, start putting small pieces of bread, cooked rice or uncooked porridge oats directly into the nest. Their mother will eat this too, but also ensure you maintain her normal food supply. When they reach two weeks old baby food can be placed on jam jar lids and put beside the nest. By now they will have started leaving the nest although their eyes will still be closed. Do not put food in a bowl for the babies as they will not be able to reach it. Gradually introduce small pieces of fresh food, such as broccoli, spinach or greens. Try to avoid foods such as lettuce that have high moisture content but low energy level. Ensure the water bottle is low enough for them to be able to reach. It is important at this time to make a fuss of their mother so she does not feel jealous or left out. If she was used to coming out of her cage regularly before giving birth, she might appreciate a welcome break from her offspring and enjoy having a run round in her ball for a short time or just to come out of her cage for a play. But don't keep her away from her babies for too long. This is the ideal opportunity to have a closer look at her babies while she is out of the cage and distracted.

It is not recommended to handle the babies during the first two weeks however tempting it might be to have a look in the nest. Newborn babies must not be out of the nest for longer than a minute or two, otherwise they can die of hypothermia because their body temperature can drop quickly. The mother may not be happy with you touching her babies and this could lead to cannibalism. If you do touch any of the babies when you are putting food in the cage, it is important that you also touch the bedding to ensure your scent becomes a natural part of her environment. In addition, gently put your hand over the other babies so that you have not singled out just one with your different scent. If the female is aggressive, do not attempt to touch her babies, as she might feel threatened.

After two weeks, the babies may be carefully and gently handled. At this stage you should handle them daily to begin the taming process; this makes them much better pets later in life. Transfer them all into a carry case and one by one pick them up for a minute or two before returning them to their nest to ensure that each one gets the same amount of handling time. At this age they will be quite nervous and jumpy so be careful when handling them in case they jump out of your hands. Always handle them at a low height in case any do fall.

At 4 weeks old, they will all be very active, climbing bars and foraging for food. They will also enjoy running in wheels. If possible fit 2 or more wheels in the cage so they can all have a run without squabbling. Be careful when using the more enclosed wheels in case 2 or 3 babies try to play at the same time thus running the risk of getting baby feet caught in the drainage slit which these wheels tend to have. At this stage and no later, it is important to sex them and separate the boys from the girls. These can then be kept together in two single-

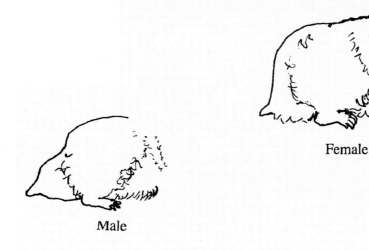

Female

Male

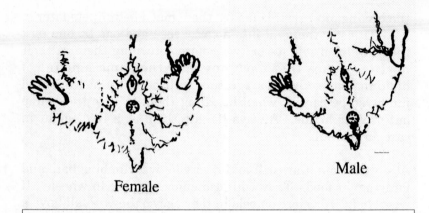

Female   Male

sex cages for another two or three weeks before they need to be re-homed into individual cages.

At 5-6 weeks, they can be re-homed. Syrians are often happy to remain together until 6-8 weeks old, but, should they start fighting around this time or if one is being picked on and is sleeping away from the others, then it is vital to separate them to prevent injury.

Russian dwarf hamsters

Campbells
Campbells are often kept in colonies so there is little extra needed to do to mate them. However, if the female that you wish to mate has been separated from males, it is important that you put her into the male's cage. Never put a male into the female's cage, as she is likely to be aggressive towards him. Keep a close watch on them and remove her if she shows signs of aggression.

The gestation period is between 18-21 days. Litter size is usually about 4 and several females will often give birth around the same time in a colony. They will put all their babies into the same nest and help each other feed them and take care of them. The males also take an active role in looking after the babies. As for Winter Whites and Roborovski hamsters, the pair will mate immediately after the birth of the litter. And similar to Syrians and other hamster varieties, they can kill their young. It is therefore vital that you ensure sufficient food and water at all times and that the tank will be big enough for the expanding colony.

Do not disturb the nest for 2 weeks after the birth otherwise the mother might reject the babies. As for Syrian hamsters, when you do handle the babies, ensure your scent is on all the babies and on the nest itself and not on just one. Unless you are planning on having an expanding colony, the babies should be sexed and separated into two single-sex cages at 3-4 weeks. They can be re-homed at 6-7 weeks of age.

Young Syrian hamsters are relatively easily sexed, especially when a number of hamsters allow comparison between the sexes. Females have two rows of dots (teats) along the abdomen that are absent in males. However, as the animals age and fur covers the teats, sexing becomes more difficult. Another general guide to sexing is by observation of the animals from the side. In the male, the tail end comes down to more of a point, whereas for the female, this is quite rounded. This feature becomes more apparent as they age. Another method is to compare the genitalia by gently turning them on their backs. All hamsters possess two openings: the anus and penis for a male and the anus and urethral opening for a female. These openings are much closer together on females than males. Once the hamsters have been sexed, they should be separated into two cages. It would be wise to check them again the following day. Mistakes are common, especially in growing animals where the external sexual characteristics may change rapidly as they develop. The last thing you would want is to put a boy in with the girls and run the risk of having a cage of pregnant females.

Winter Whites
Winter Whites do not usually breed until 8 weeks old and females do not accept males easily so breeding can be technically demanding.

If you are planning to breed Winter Whites, keep a male and female together from birth, although you should not breed from this pair if they are brother and sister. When a female has been used to being in a cage with her brother you stand more chance of successfully introducing her and mating her with another male, although this is still not guaranteed. Once separated completely from males for any period of time, the female is unlikely to accept a male.

Introduce the female to the male and leave them together for a few days, separating them if they are aggressive towards each other. If the female becomes aggressive during pregnancy it is worth separating the male. Not only does this minimise the likelihood of injury, but also prevents them from mating again as soon as the litter is born.

Following a successful mating gestation is between 18-21 days and the average litter size is up to 10. The female will mate again on the same day as giving birth.

Winter Whites are extremely protective of their newborn and the mother may be aggressive to any other offspring in the tank if threatened. Once the litter is about 3-4 weeks old, they should be separated from her if she has become pregnant again to avoid injuries as sometimes the mother turns on her babies if she is pregnant with another litter or has another litter to look after. The babies can also start fighting, in which case they may need to be separated.

When there is more than one female in the nest the oldest will be dominant and will be the one to mate. Squabbles do occur when there are new babies.
If you want to handle the offspring, it is vital a lot of attention is also given to the 'mum' or otherwise she might become jealous and aggressive towards them.

Campbell colonies breed well, but Winter Whites tend to breed better in pairs.

Roborovskis
Roborovskis tend not to mate if they feel stressed. There are several such stresses but the presence of another pair in the tank is a common one. After a period of attempted breeding, if there is no sign of any babies arriving, then any other pairs present should be removed to their own tanks or put on

another separated level in the same tank. This allows each pair to create their own territory and may be the only trigger needed for successful mating and breeding.

Introduction of Roborovski hamsters to each other is very difficult. Often, the initial introduction may look a success only to find the male being picked on later. If there are any signs of scratches or bites, separate them immediately.

They can breed from as young as 3 months although often they are older than this. There is a tendency to seasonal breeding with the peak in spring and summer. They mate again on the same day as giving birth. It is worth noting that consecutive litters can be aggressive towards each other. Hamsters that continually breed are likely to eventually cannibalise their young.

On average, the gestation period for Roborovski hamsters is 21 days with an average litter of 3-5.

Two pairs of Roborovskis were kept in the same tank. For several months they lived together, one couple mainly occupying the upper level, the other pair living in the lower level. Neither pair mated. The pairs were separated and put into tanks of their own. Almost immediately both pairs mated and produced litters.

Chinese hamsters

It is possible to introduce male and female Chinese hamsters but care must be taken when doing this and they should be monitored closely to ensure that they do not fight. Always put the female in with the male or introduce them in neutral territory to reduce aggression. A young female with a slightly older bigger male can work well.

The gestation period for Chinese hamsters is 21 days and the litter size can vary from a single baby up to 7, although the average is about 3 or 4. Generally there are no problems with the birth itself and the male is allowed to re-enter the nest after a couple of days in order to share responsibility for looking after the babies. As with Russian hamsters, they are likely to mate immediately after the babies are born. The babies can be sexed and separated at 28 days.

Some Words of Warning

* *Never mate brother and sister as the temperament of offspring can be affected.*

* *Never mate Campbells with Winter Whites. A female Winter White is unlikely to be able to give birth to Campbell babies, as they are too big for her. The hybrid babies are usually sterile.*

* *Do not breed dwarf hamsters in cages with bars and wire shelves. The offspring are very small and can get stuck between bars and injure themselves.*

* *Do not overfeed pregnant hamsters, as their babies can grow too big. This can result in difficulties during the birth process. As soon as the babies are born the mother can be fed bread and milk, or porridge.*

* *Do not breed from any hamster that has an illness that can be passed onto their offspring.*

* *Do not over-breed from any pair otherwise the health of the female and that of her offspring may be compromised.*

* *Avoid mating a female once she has reached 1 year old as in hamster years she has reached middle age.*

* *Wait until the female is at least 12 weeks old before first mating.*

Chapter 6

Veterinary Care of your Hamster

Welfare of animals
In the last century several laws were passed to protect the welfare of animals, including those kept as pets. These laws include the Protection of Animals Act of 1911, the Protection of Animals (Amendment) Act of 1965, the Veterinary Surgeons (Exemptions) Order of 1962 and the Veterinary Surgeons Act of 1966.

Whilst most people do not need a law to advise them on the responsibility they are taking on when acquiring a pet, sadly, sometimes, even the best intentions of a pet owner can cause the unnecessary suffering of an animal. Failure to provide appropriate veterinary care and attention are classed as an offence under the 1911 Protection of Animals Act.

It is therefore vital that any small animal (or large for that matter) suspected of having anything wrong with it is taken to a vet. A quick diagnosis and treatment can often mean the difference between life and death and certainly will reduce any suffering in the meantime.

The Role of your Vet
Once you have purchased your new hamster, there are some important groups of people you need to get to know. These

include a good pet shop as a source of the best quality food and safest equipment. Getting to know other friends who also have hamsters and who share your interests will be beneficial as it might be possible to come to some arrangement to look after each other's pets during holidays. You will also need to find a vet who has a special interest in these small creatures and whose advice you can rely on in those worrying times of illness that may lie ahead. Choose carefully as you will hopefully get to know your vet very well over many happy years of keeping hamsters. You can also discuss with your vet the situation should you need advice after-hours if your pet is poorly. Remember that Syrian hamsters tend not to rally round until late evening and often after the standard veterinary surgery times, therefore illness may not be detected until then which might mean calling out an emergency vet.

Spotting Illness
Before even considering the different types of illnesses that can affect your hamster, the most important task of all is to spot that your pet is ill in the first place. This can only be accomplished by really getting to know your individual pet - how it looks, how it behaves, how much it eats and drinks as well as the changes to its body as it grows and develops. This will help to avoid panic visits to your vet for emergencies such as lumps growing below the tail area that turn out to be normal testicles or tumours on the flanks that turn out to be normal hip scent glands. Any change from this can then easily be identified and investigated. Syrian hamsters, for example, due to their nocturnal lifestyle, may not be seen by the owner until late in the evening, and some days not at all. Therefore illnesses sometimes go undetected for several days. Also, due to the small size of these animals, illness affects them far more dramatically than for a larger animal. After all, due to their short lifespan, a single day for a hamster may be the equivalent of a few weeks for a human. Therefore,

with some acute illnesses, a hamster's condition can deteriorate rapidly over a couple of hours or a tumour may almost be seen growing day by day. It is wise to spend a little time each day just observing and enjoying your new friend with its odd habits and funny little ways.

Investigating Illness

Once you have decided that your pet is ill, you will need to investigate the problem to decide what you can do to help or whether you need to take your pet to the vet. To aid in this task, a breakdown of some of the types of diseases that can affect your hamster are given in Chapter 7, along with some possible approaches to treatment.

Treating your own pet

As a pet owner, you are allowed to treat your own pet, provided you do not cause it any unnecessary suffering. Misdiagnosis by an owner that delays essential and correct treatment can cause suffering. Therefore, the importance of taking ill pets to a veterinary surgeon early in the disease process cannot be stressed enough. As stated above, failure to provide appropriate veterinary care and attention are classed as an offence under the 1911 Protection of Animals Act.

It is important to remember that it is dangerous to share another animal's medication with your hamster since certain drugs that may be safe for other animals are toxic for hamsters. For example, eye drops that may have been prescribed for your cat or dog could be totally unsuitable to use on a hamster and may make any eye disease much worse. It is also worth remembering that only a veterinary surgeon can prescribe medications listed as Prescription Only Medications (POM) and that these medications must be used only on those animals specified on the label.

With more and more information being accessible on the Internet it is also tempting to order medicines advertised on the various Websites. When ordering from a non-UK Website, the medicines may not be licensed or legal in this country and furthermore, by the time the medicine arrives, it could be too late for your pet.

There are, however, many first aid and home-care approaches that you can carry out as a pet owner, many of which are covered in this text.

Veterinary treatment

Things have moved on rapidly with regard to the veterinary care of hamsters and other small animals in recent years with the result that they can now be treated up to the same level of veterinary expertise as applies to dogs and cats. This may, however, involve expensive laboratory tests and surgical materials. So it is important to have planned in advance of your veterinary visit how far you wish to ask your vet to go in the treatment of your individual pet. This is especially important where a child is involved. Account should be taken of the expected remaining lifespan for the pet, the general quality of life of the pet after treatment and the risk of failure of treatment, to help you make any decisions. Remember that euthanasia may be a better and pain-free option that immediately prevents further suffering (see Chapter 9).

Scheduling a Veterinary Appointment

Most veterinary practices these days work on an appointment basis which allows you to plan your visit and thus to get the most benefit from it. Since hamsters are nocturnal, your vet may see only a sleepy hamster at a morning appointment, which makes diagnosis more difficult so requesting an afternoon or evening appointment is advisable.

Provided that the hamster lives in a portable wire cage, then it is best to take the hamster along in its own cage. Do not clean out the cage before the visit. This allows the veterinary surgeon to observe the animal's natural behaviour in its own environment. It also allows the vet to assess any problems that there may be with the environment itself and also to check the animal's droppings, water source, bedding and food. Do empty the water bottle before travelling though. Because these bottles are gravity fed, the vibrations during travel will make them leak leading to wet bedding. Should the animals be housed in cages that are too large to carry or in glass tanks, then smaller carrying cases are available that are ideal for a visit to the vet. In colony situations where only one animal seems ill, it may be worth bringing the rest of the colony along as well. This allows the veterinary surgeon to assess for evidence of inheritable conditions that also affects others in the colony and for the spread of contagious disease. Furthermore, the risk of rejection on return of the ill animal to the rest of the colony is reduced because all animals will have been exposed to the same novel smells so the sick one will not be singled out.

Have all the information your vet is likely to require prepared in your mind or written down in advance. This will include the age and sex of the patient, when and where you got the hamster, any other pets you have and whether these show any signs of illness. As for the specific illness itself, be ready to tell the vet exactly the symptoms you have noticed, when these started, whether they are getting worse and whether you have attempted any home-care prior to the visit.

Glossary of Veterinary Terminology

Your veterinary surgeon will undoubtedly explain all your options in language that is understandable. However, brief descriptions of some of these terms are given in this section.

ABDOMEN: that part of the body behind the rib cage and in front of the pelvis,

ABSCESS: an accumulation of pus in an abscess cavity contained by an abscess wall.

ACUTE: rapid in onset, short and severe.

ADMINISTRATION: the giving of drugs to an animal.

ALLERGY: over-reaction of the immune system to an agent that should not normally cause disease.

ALOPECIA: hair loss that is abnormal.

AMPUTATION: the surgical removal of an extremity such as a leg.

ANALGESIC: drug to reduce or eliminate pain. Administration may be by injections or by drops given orally or tablets to be crushed into the food.

ANTIBIOTIC: drug administered to an animal to treat specifically bacterial disease. Your vet may well have begun the course of treatment with an injection but you will likely need to continue the course, using antibiotics added to the drinking water, given orally or added to the food.

ANTIFUNGAL: drug used in the treatment of fungal disease such as ringworm.

ANTI-INFLAMMATORY: drug to reduce pain, redness, heat and swelling.

ANTISEPTIC: chemical used to kill microorganisms on the skin of living animals.

AQUEOUS: water-based.

BACTERIA: microscopic organisms that can cause disease such as Tyzzer's disease.

BACTERICIDAL: drug capable of directly killing bacteria without the help of the immune system.

BACTERIOSTATIC: drug that stops bacteria from multiplying while awaiting the natural defence mechanisms of the body to kill them.

BIOPSY: removal of a small piece of tissue from a living animal for laboratory testing.

BLOOD TEST: blood samples can be taken from your hamster but the small volume that can safely be taken does limit the information gained. This is a technique that is more frequently used in laboratory animals. Blood samples are useful in the diagnosis of such serious conditions as diabetes.

BROAD SPECTRUM: drug capable of affecting a wide range of organisms.

CAUTERISATION: the application of treatments to help stop bleeding. For example, when a nail has been cut too short or been broken, ferric chloride or silver nitrate are two of the agents used.

CASTRATION: also called 'neutering', castration refers to the removal of the testicles in a male. This may be necessary if they become cancerous, to stop further breeding in a mixed colony of males and females or to reduce aggression.

CATARACT: loss of lens transparency in the eyeball giving a white colour to the normally dark pupil of the eye.

CHRONIC: slow in onset and progressing over a prolonged period of time.

CONGENITAL: present from birth.

CONJUNCTIVITIS: the inflammation of the lining of the insides of the eyelids.

CONSTIPATION: production of abnormally firm faeces that are difficult to pass.

CONTAGIOUS: a disease that can easily be spread from a sick hamster to infect a healthy one.

CORNEA: transparent layer covering the front of the eyeball.

CREMATION: disposal of a dead body by incineration at a registered crematorium.

CYST: fluid-filled cavity or sac.

DEHYDRATION: reduction in the water content of the body to the point where it results in damage to health e.g. via diarrhoea.

DERMATITIS: inflammation of the skin leading to symptoms such as itching, hair loss, redness and skin thickening.

DIABETES TEST: certain strains of hamster (e.g. Campbells) seem to have a tendency of developing diabetes.

This means they have excessively high blood glucose leading to increased urine volume and thirst. Blood samples or urine testing can diagnose it by checking for raised glucose levels.

DIARRHOEA: passing faeces that is higher in water content than is normal.

DISEASE: any deviation from total normal health of an animal.

DISINFECTANT: chemical used to kill micro-organisms on inanimate objects such as cages.

DIURETIC: drug causing increased urine production.

DRUG: any chemical used to treat disease.

ELECTROLYTES: various salts within the body such as sodium and potassium.

EUTHANASIA: painlessly helping an animal to die. It can also be called 'putting to sleep' and is usually carried out by administering either an injected or inhaled anaesthetic.

EXCISION: removal of part of the body by cutting it away.

FAECES: also called 'stools' or 'solid toilet', refers to the material evacuated from the anus.

FEVER: body temperature being above normal levels, usually as a result of viral or bacterial infections.

FRACTURE: snapped or broken bone.

FUNGUS: Mould-like organisms that may cause disease such as ringworm.

GANGRENE: death of part of the body due to a lack of blood supply.

GENERAL ANAESTHESIA: putting an animal into a deep sleep, during which they feel no pain but from which they can be woken up at any time. It is usually accomplished by giving the animal a special gas to breathe but can also be done by injection. It allows a fuller examination than may be possible awake, the taking of X-rays or surgery to be performed. There is always a risk that the animal may go into too deep a sleep leading to death. In this event, an animal would not have felt any pain. The risk of anaesthetic death rises as the pet ages, as the animal becomes sicker and as the duration and complexity of surgery increases.

GLAUCOMA: enlargement of the eyeball due to increased fluid within the eyeball.

HISTOPATHOLOGY: laboratory tests performed on tissue samples taken from the body.

HORMONE: chemical produced naturally in one part of the body that affects the function of some other part of the body.

HYPERTHERMIA: disease resulting from elevation of body temperature too far above normal levels.

HYPOTHERMIA: disease resulting from the body temperature dropping too far below normal levels.

IMMUNE SYSTEM: those organs and cells in the body that help to protect against specific disease organisms.

IMMUNO-SUPPRESSIVE: having the effect of lowering the natural immune system of the body.

INCISION: to surgically cut into the body.

INCIZORS: the paired long upper and lower teeth at the front of the mouth.

INFECTION: the presence in the body of microorganisms that can cause disease such as bacteria, viruses or fungi.

INJECTION: administration of a medication using a syringe and needle to 'inject' it through the skin into the body itself.

INFLAMMATION: the response of the body to any injury, resulting in heat, swelling, pain and redness of the affected area. The names of disease states where inflammation is involved usually end in the letters '-itis', such as dermatitis or conjunctivitis.

ISOTONIC: containing the same balance of electrolytes as the body.

MAMMARY GLANDS: breast tissue along the tummy that produces milk.

MANGE: skin disease resulting from the multiplication of mites in the skin.

MASTITIS: inflammation and infection of the mammary glands.

MICRO-ORGANISM: living creatures that are too small to see with the naked eye and require a microscope to view them, such as bacteria.

MUCOUS MEMBRANE: delicate lining to the eyelids, respiratory tract, digestive tract and urinary system.

OBESITY: the state of being above the ideal body weight to the point where disease is likely to result.

OESTRUS: also called 'being in season', 'on heat' or 'the receptive period', the period of time when a female will allow a male to mate. The regular pattern of going in and out of oestrus is called the 'oestrous cycle'.

OVARIO-HYSTERECTOMY: also called 'neutering', ovario-hysterectomy refers to the removal of the ovaries and uterus. This has the effect of permanently stopping the hamster from showing signs of coming into season and from breeding. It may be necessary in the case of ovarian cysts or uterine cancer.

PARASITE: organism that lives in or on another and results in disease.

PARALYSIS: loss of use of part of the body, usually a limb, due to damage to a nerve supplying that area.

PELVIS: the bone frame of the hip area.

PERITONEUM: The cavity contained within the abdomen.

P.O.M.: Prescription Only Medication. This is a legally controlled drug that can only be prescribed by a veterinary surgeon.

POST-MORTEM: literally means 'after death' and usually refers to the examination of a dead body to ascertain the cause of death.

PROBIOTIC: source of live bacteria that can multiply within the body without causing disease and deters multiplication of harmful bacteria.

PROGNOSIS: refers to the likely future outcome of a current disease.

PRURITUS: skin itchiness/ irritation.

PUS: accumulation of creamy liquid in an abscess, usually as a result of bacterial infection.

PYOMETRA: infection of the uterus resulting in an accumulation of pus.

RADIOGRAPHY: the process of taking x-rays.

REHYDRATION: administration of fluids to reverse dehydration.

RINGWORM TEST: ringworm is the disease resulting from growth of a fungus on the skin or nails leading to nail or hair loss. It is contagious to humans and can be diagnosed by a laboratory test on hair or nail samples taken from the affected area. A quick but less reliable test is to shine an ultraviolet lamp on the lesion, which may glow bright green if it is ringworm positive.

SEPTICAEMIA: multiplication of bacteria in the blood stream, usually resulting in severe acute disease.

SKIN SCRAPE: literally means scraping off the outer layers of skin with a blade until the skin starts to ooze blood. These samples are then checked under a microscope for the presence of mites.

STITCHES: skin wounds after surgery can be sutured with either stitches that need removal or those that are dissolvable without removal. The latter are preferable since most hamsters will rapidly chew out any stitches that leave knots present on the outside of the skin. Alternatively, small wounds can be closed using specialised tissue glue.

SYMPTOMS: the external signs of disease shown by a sick animal.

SYNTHETIC: man-made, not natural.

SYSTEMIC: medication that travels from the site of application all around the body.

THERAPEUTIC: capable of effecting therapy or cure.

THORAX: that part of the body covered by the rib cage.

TOPICAL: application of a medication directly to the skin.

TOURNIQUET: a band tightened around a limb to the point where it restricts blood supply to the tip of the limb.

TOXICITY: poisoning.

TUMOUR: also be called a 'cancer', 'mass' or 'growth'. Tumour refers to a part of the body that grows faster than the body requires and results in the formation of an abnormal lump.

UTERUS: the womb or organ where unborn baby hamsters develop within the mother hamster.

VIRUS: microscopic organisms that can cause disease and are easily spread between hamsters such as cold viruses.

X-RAY: specialised type of photograph of the inside of an animal. A general anaesthetic is usually required to prevent movement that blurs the picture. X-rays allow your vet to check for broken bones as well as many other abnormalities inside your pet.

ZOONOSIS: a disease that can spread from animals to humans.

Glossary of Homeopathic Terminology

ANTIOPATHY: System of medicine utilising agents whose action is opposite to the symptoms. Most modern conventional medicines are often used in this way. This is palliative and may be suppressive in its direct action on signs and symptoms.

CONCOMITANT SYMPTOM: A symptom that accompanies the major presenting symptom and is a useful aid to prescribing homeopathically.

CONSTITUTIONAL REMEDY/MEDICINE: One that takes the entire make-up of the patient into account, rather than just the presenting signs and symptoms.

CONVENTIONAL MEDICINE: A term to describe what is presently taught in veterinary schools, with regard to the use of modern drug medicines.

HOMEOPATHY: The treatment of disease with a substance that has the power to produce, in a healthy body, signs and symptoms similar to those displayed by the patient.

HOMEOPROPHYLAXIS: The prevention of disease (usually infectious), using a medicine that has a symptom picture similar to that disease (e.g. homeopathic to it).

ISOPATHY: The treatment of disease by the identical agent of the disease. Here vaccination has similarities.

NOSODE: A nosode is a medicine made in the usual homeopathic way, but it is prepared from disease material, e.g. tissue, discharges, secretions. It may be used in the treatment or homeoprophylaxis of infectious disease.

PALLIATIVE: Treatment aimed at directly reducing symptoms (antiopathy).

SIDE EFFECTS: The reaction of the body to antiopathic drug medication. These are any unwanted effects following treatment.

Chapter 7

Diseases of Hamsters

Introduction

This chapter deals with some diseases that affect hamsters. It is important to remember that more than one disease state can affect a hamster at any one time and that the presence of one disease may lead to the development of other conditions. For example, your hamster may have symptoms that lead to a diagnosis of possible mange. However, the development of mange may be linked with underlying kidney disease or tumours so treatment for the mange alone would not resolve the overall problem. It is also important to stress that the information in this chapter is provided to help you care for your hamster and to prevent suffering but only a veterinary surgeon has all the skills and experience to properly diagnose and treat your hamster.

There are obviously almost infinite lists of diseases that can affect hamsters so only those that occur commonly are given here. A quick guide to help you link a symptom your hamster may show to possible diseases is given in Appendix III at the back of this book.

Diseases are grouped according to the organ systems of the body affected. Information is provided on each disease in a standard format to facilitate the understanding of each specific disease. Each disease section covers causes, symptoms, treatment and the outlook or prognosis. Where appropriate, other information is included such as alternative treatments, prevention of recurrence and any risk of spread to humans. Disease names are followed by a code indicating the severity of the condition and how urgent it is to seek veterinary intervention, as detailed below.

Code	Interpretation
*	Treatable at home/Non emergency
**	Non emergency but take to vet if condition persists
***	Take to a vet within next day or two
****	Emergency - Immediate veterinary treatment essential

It is important to stress again that this is just a guide and that, if in doubt, it is safest to get your vet to examine your hamster in case there are other factors that you have missed. In most cases, the prognosis is as much dependent on the speed at which treatment is begun, as it is by the condition itself, so it is wise not to delay in seeking veterinary attention whenever your pet is ill.

Homeopathic medicines provide a very gentle, safe and effective form of therapy in many disease conditions and where they are appropriate, details have been included. They are ideally suited to small mammals and they can be given alongside conventional veterinary medication. Due to the mechanism of action of homeopathic remedies, this cannot adversely influence the conventional input but may result in less effective homeopathic benefit. This means that homeopathic medication may be used in emergencies, before the vet is able to see the patient. It also means that, should conventional methods have failed to help, homeopathic methods can be employed with the hope of finding a solution to the problem. Homeopathic remedies are available without prescription from most good health stops and chemists.

Diseases Affecting The Head

Overgrown Teeth ***
Causes: Hamsters have two upper and two lower orange-coloured front teeth or incisors that grow continuously throughout life. Hamsters routinely gnaw resulting in the upper incisors wearing down the lowers. The lower incisors are normally three times the length of their upper incisors and are naturally very long. This comes as a surprise to most people on first inspection of hamster dentition since the teeth of most other domestic pets have uppers and lowers of equal size.

Again, the moral is to spend time learning what is normal for your hamster during health and thus avoid panic when something 'strange' is noticed later. If these teeth grow into the wrong position or if the hamster does not gnaw enough, then the incisors will get too long. This may be congenital or result from dental injury from falling or from chewing the bars of the cage or from a diet too low in calcium such as a high proportion of sunflower seeds leading to weakened teeth. If one incisor is broken or missing, the opposite one will overgrow due to lack of wear. The molars (hind teeth) do not grow continuously in hamsters and thus are rarely a cause of clinical problems.

It should be noted that occasionally a hamster may develop no incisor teeth or those that do develop may fall out and not be replaced. This is not a major problem so long as it is noticed early and the diet is altered. Affected individuals will not be able to split and chew normal hamster food. Instead, regular hamster food should be put through a blender and have added water until a soft consistency is achieved. Alternatively, vegetarian baby food can be used. These hamsters are often normal in every other way and, in fact, may make even better pets since the element of the surprise bite has been removed!

Symptoms: Overgrown teeth interfere with the ability to eat and the hamster may lose weight. The elongated teeth may penetrate into the gums of the opposite jaw causing severe pain and infection and a resultant drooling of saliva. Secondary infection may cause a bad smell to emanate from the mouth area. An examination of the mouth while holding the hamster by the scruff will easily show up the problem.

Treatment: Hamsters with overgrown incisors will usually require their teeth clipped with small clippers or to have them burred down with a dental drill on a regular basis. Your vet should initially do this but you may be happy to repeat this at home after your vet has shown you the technique. Antibiotics may be required if there is infection present. Gnawing on hard diets that are a rich source of calcium is advisable e.g. dog biscuits. This should delay recurrence of the problem or hopefully even prevent it in the first instance. Wooden toys and chewing blocks can also be purchased from the pet shop to help keep teeth in trim or branches of trees such as apple are equally useful.

Prognosis: The outlook for affected hamsters is usually good so long as the condition is spotted early and is treated properly and regularly. Affected animals should not be used for breeding.

Homeopathic treatment: *Calc. phos.* and *Calc. fluor.* Schuessler Tissue Salts do a *Calc. phos. 6x*, which can be very useful for regular dosage, on a preventive basis.

Tooth Root Abscess/ Caries ***

Causes: Hamsters are prone to periodontal disease and tooth rot just as for humans. The problem is exacerbated if they are fed a diet rich in sweet and sticky items. Infection can track down outside or inside the tooth to the root where an abscess will develop.

Symptoms: Since the tooth root where the abscess occurs is positioned just below the eye, a swelling may develop on the face at this position. The tooth will be painful and you may notice the hamster reluctant to eat or showing signs of pain when eating or drooling saliva from the mouth.

Treatment: The abscess itself can be opened and drained as described in the section on abscesses followed by treatment with antibiotics such as enrofloxacin or marbofloxacin. However, since the source of the infection was the tooth, permanent resolution of the problem will only be achieved by extraction of all affected teeth under general anaesthesia by your veterinary surgeon. These affected teeth are often quite loose and this is not as difficult a procedure as might be expected.

Prognosis: So long as affected teeth can be removed, the prognosis should be good. It is important to remove any sugary or sticky items from the diet to prevent recurrence. Hard treats such as hard dog biscuits keep the hamster occupied and help to wear down the teeth, keeping them healthy but without encouraging caries.

Homeopathic treatment: The treatment most likely to help with healing of an abscess, perhaps avoiding the need for antibiotic, is a combination of *Mercurius solubilis 30c* and *Hepar sulphuris 30c*. To aid in the prevention of caries, use tissue salts, as for overgrown teeth above. If there is pain from decay, consider *Natrum carbonicum 6c*.

Impaction of the Cheek Pouches ***

Causes: Hamsters have a large muscular sac inside each cheek that extends back as far as the shoulder. These are used for transporting food, bedding material and occasionally even their babies. Feeding sticky treats (especially children's sweets) to hamsters may result in the pouches becoming jammed with this type of material. Attempts by the hamster to empty the sacs will result in self-mutilation and secondary infection. Abnormal dentition (teeth) may also contribute to cheek pouch impaction. Seeds with husks should not be fed as they can embed into the cheek pouch lining resulting in infections especially by Streptococcus and Staphylococcus bacteria.

Symptoms: Swellings will be seen on either side of the face that do not disappear regularly as would a normal full cheek pouch. When infection is present, the facial area will emit a foul smell and the hamster may stop eating, look uncomfortable and drool saliva. Attempts by the hamster to empty the sacs can result in self-mutilation to the facial area.

Treatment: This condition really needs to be treated by a vet. An anaesthetic is likely to be required before the pouches are manually emptied and treated with local antiseptics or antibiotics. Systemic antibiotics such as enrofloxacin are also likely to be administered.

Prognosis: Provided treatment is commenced early, there is every chance of a full recovery. Prevention is by avoidance of sticky foods, especially 'human' sweets. Some pet treats such as pet-chocolate and yoghurt drops can also cause problems for your hamster if they don't empty their cheek pouches regularly.

Homeopathic treatment: *Merc. sol.*; also wash out mouth with *Calendula lotion*.

114

Eversion of the Cheek Pouches ***
Causes: The cheek pouches may evert or turn themselves inside out and protrude from the mouth of the hamster spontaneously. Alternatively, if a sticky food item has been fed, the hamster may evert the pouches in its attempt to remove the offending item.

Symptoms: The everted pouch will be seen protruding from the side of the mouth as a pink mass of tissue.

Treatment: Treatment for eversion should be by a veterinary surgeon. Attempts to replace the pouch in a conscious animal are likely to result in damage to the pouch and repeat eversion later. Your vet will sedate or anaesthetise the hamster before replacing the pouch into its natural position and suturing it in place to prevent recurrence.

Prognosis: Once replaced and sutured in place, the prognosis should be good.

Homeopathic treatment: No special treatment.

Conjunctivitis***
Causes: Conjunctivitis refers to inflammation of the insides of the eyelids and can have many causes. These include viral and bacterial infections, allergic conditions to bedding for example, or tiny bits of irritants getting under the eyelids such as bits of sawdust. Hamsters naturally have bulging eyes that make it easier for irritants to affect them. Some hamsters develop this condition due to having eyelids that are turned in towards the eyeball and rub on the eyeball every time the hamster blinks. This is called entropian.

Symptoms: The hamster will show a discharge from one or both eyes that may even cause the eyelids to stick together. The eyes will look red. Because conjunctivitis is painful, the hamster may squint or rub at the eyes and will be dull and look unwell.

Note: It is important to be aware that hamsters often show 'sticky eyes', where the eyelids stick to each other, as part of the signs of any generalised disease process. Thus, the presence of this symptom alone does not prove that the problem is just conjunctivitis.

Treatment: The treatment will depend on the specific cause. If a foreign body is present, it may be washed out with cooled boiled water. If it is allergic in origin, then bedding/air fresheners/etc. should be changed and corticosteroid eye drops such as Maxitrol Drops may be required. For bacterial infections, antibiotic eye drops such as Tiacil Ophthalmic Solution (Virbac Limited) or ointment such as Fucithalmic Vet (Leo Animal Health) will be needed. For entropian, surgery could be attempted to turn out the eyelids and stop them rubbing on the eyeball but a lifetime of application of eye ointments to protect the eyeball is a more likely option.

Prognosis: The prognosis is generally good if the specific cause can be found and if treatment begins before the disease has permanently damaged the eye itself. In cases of entropian, affected animals should not be used for breeding. Remember that old or sick hamsters may show sticky eyelids as part of the overall disease symptoms but without the conjunctivitis being their most important problem.

Allergy or irritation from bedding materials is a common contributory factor and it is always wise to look for an alternative. Try using a different brand of wood chippings or stop using chippings completely, covering the floor of the cage with paper bedding instead. This will mean your pet will need to be cleaned out more regularly but it will reduce the build up of ammonia gas and the potentially irritant scent of pine. Alternatively, you may buy your hamster a 'designer' toilet and put this in the corner they normally use as a toilet with some soiled material placed inside it. Some hamsters very quickly get into the routine of using this and it is easy to wash out daily.

Do not use air fresheners, especially the plug-in variety, in the room housing the hamster. Carpet shampoos and strong smelling upholstery cleaners might also cause problems for them and should be avoided, as should cigarette smoke.

Homeopathic treatment: Euphrasia lotion, diluted one drop in an egg-cup full of boiled cooled water; also, by mouth (or via drinking water), homeopathic Pulsatilla. Many different homeopathic remedies may prove useful, however, depending upon the exact signs shown. Expert homeopathic veterinary help may be needed if these suggestions fail.

Alternative treatment: Aloe Vera can be used in treating this condition. However, it is important your vet diagnoses the problem specifically before treatment commences.

"Bleeding" Eyes**

In common with most other rodents, Hamsters have special glands behind their eyeballs called Harderian Glands. These glands produce a reddish material that may look like blood but is not. Its purpose is to act as an ocular lubricant and it tends to be produced in greater quantities when the hamster is unwell for any reason, but especially if they have viral diseases. The red material can be cleaned daily with cooled boiled water on a soft piece of tissue paper. Although the eyes are not really bleeding, these hamsters are often unwell for some other reason so it is still wise to give any such hamster a complete health check. If it does look unwell, it should be taken to your vet.

Prolapse/ Rupture of the Eyeball ****

Causes: Prolapse of the eyeball refers to the whole eyeball coming out of its socket and rupture refers to the eyeball bursting. Both may occur together. The cause may be from fighting or from rough handling especially if the animal has been held by the scruff too tightly. Hamsters naturally have bulging eyeballs. This probably allows the animal a more panoramic view in the wild to spot predators but it does make prolapse of the eyeball easier to occur.

Symptoms: These are obvious as the eyeball will either be dangling outside its socket or popped and collapsed.

Treatment: Should the eyeball be ruptured, it may be possible to just treat with antibiotics such as enrofloxacin to prevent infection and to let the eye socket fill in with scar tissue without surgery. Alternatively the eyeball may need to be removed. In the case of a prolapse, it may be possible to replace the eye into the socket if the animal is taken to a vet soon enough and provided the eye has not been damaged. Your vet may need to perform an operation to suture the eyelids closed for a week to help the eyeball stay in the socket while healing occurs or you may be required to apply an eye ointment such as Fucithalmic (Leo Laboratories Limited) to the eye several times daily to prevent infection and to keep the eye moist.

Prognosis: Provided the eye can be rapidly and gently replaced into the socket, then it can be salvaged. Prevention of recurrence is very important, as this is a most distressing condition for both the animal and the owner. It is advisable to isolate affected individuals in a cage of their own if fighting has caused the problem. Be careful when restraining any hamster by holding the scruff. This method should really only be used when attempting to steady them to have their teeth or nails clipped, or when the vet is examining them. Train them to walk on your hand, or pick them up by scooping them from underneath.

Homeopathic treatment: *Symphytum, Arnica* and *Ruta* can all play a part in minimising permanent damage to the eye. If ulceration is present, *Merc. corr.* is invaluable in the early stages, often doing away with the need for other help

Cataracts *
Causes: Cataracts describe the normally transparent lens within the eye becoming cloudy and white. It may be just a feature of ageing as in many humans or a symptom of diabetes.

Symptoms: A cloudy white coloration replaces the normal black colour to the pupil of the eye. Vision for the hamster will become distorted more and more as the cataract gets whiter. However since hamster vision is naturally poor anyway, this may be of little significance.

Treatment: In theory, the faulty lens could be removed from the eye, just as for larger animals and man. However, the technical difficulties plus the debatable benefits of surgery for a species where eyesight is naturally poor make this an unlikely choice of treatment. As a result, no treatment is commonly given for the cataracts themselves.

Since the cataracts are likely to further reduce the sight in a species already known for their poor vision, the environment should be made safer. Single level cages reduce fall accidents. Greater care should be taken when first approaching the hamster, as it is more likely to be scared and bite if it cannot properly visualise your approach. However, as hamster vision is naturally poor and their nocturnal nature means they rely more on other senses, there is often little change seen in the behaviour of hamsters with cataracts. It is important not to move around the cage furniture as the animals build up a mental picture of their surroundings to navigate themselves safely. Hamsters also use scents applied to the environment to help negotiate their way around. This needs to be taken into account when cleaning the cage and its furniture. Affected hamsters should, however, be tested for diabetes as described in the relevant section.

Prognosis: For age related cataracts, the prognosis is the same as for any older hamster while many diabetic hamsters live for several months with no treatment.

Homeopathic treatment: *Silica*, in 6c or 6x (Schuessler Tissue Salt) potency, can prove useful in lessening or delaying cataract formation.

Glaucoma ***
Causes: Glaucoma refers to an increased amount of fluid within the eyeball leading to swelling of the entire eyeball and loss of vision. It is relatively common in Campbell's hamsters and is thought to be a genetically inherited disease.

Symptoms: The symptoms relate to an increased fluid volume within the eye. The eye will appear enlarged. Some hamsters will show pain and rub at the eye leading to secondary infections. Occasionally, the eye will get so big that it prolapses from the socket. One or both eyes may be affected.

Treatment: There is no specific treatment for the glaucoma itself. Painkillers such as meloxicam may be required if severe discomfort is shown. Alternatively, the affected eye can be surgically removed. Affected eyes lose vision as the delicate layers on the inside of the eye that are responsible for vision are irreparably damaged by the pressure increase.

Prognosis: The prognosis for vision is poor but this is not a big problem as hamster vision is poor anyway. Since the disease may be genetically inherited, affected hamsters and close relatives should not be used for breeding.

Homeopathic treatment: The homeopathic treatment of choice is *Belladonna 30c*. This can be given up to three times daily, under close monitoring from your veterinary surgeon.

Microphthalmia/ Anophthalmia *

Causes: These diseases are congenital and genetic and are inherited as a recessive gene. These are usually seen in white individuals.

Symptoms: Microphthalmia refers to the eyes and eyelid openings being very small. Anophthalmia means the total absence of eyes and occurs especially in Campbell's. Affected babies are called 'eyeless whites'. They are often the product of breeding two mottled Campbells or two from the mottled line. Microphthalmia can be inherited in two genetic forms: homozygote or heterozygote. Homozygotes describe where the defective gene has been inherited from both parents. These animals usually die within 3 weeks of birth. Heterozygotes describe inheritance of the gene from just one parent resulting in an animal with symptoms but that survives.

Treatment: No treatment is usually given. In the case of microphthalmia, should discomfort result from the eyelids rubbing on the cornea, then application of soothing eye ointments (e.g.VISCOTEARS Novartis Ophthalmics) may help.

Prognosis: Since hamsters are nocturnal and naturally have poor eyesight anyway, these conditions are not too serious in themselves. Affected individuals and their close relatives should not be used for breeding to avoid passing on this 'anophthalmic white' gene.

Homeopathic treatment: No treatment is available, except for the prevention or reduction of secondary conjunctivitis (q.v.).

Diseases Affecting the Skin

Age-Related or Hormonal Alopecia **
Causes: Alopecia refers to abnormal hair loss for any reason. There are many hormones that affect hair and skin growth. Some are specific such as overactive adrenal glands or under-active thyroids but most are non-specific and not often specifically diagnosed. Most of these conditions are linked with ageing with estimates of 50% of hamsters over 2 years of age developing tumours of the adrenal glands. Low protein diets (less than 16% protein) that can occur if the animals overeat cereals can lead to non-specific hair-loss.

Symptoms: In health, hair follicles follows a regular pattern of growth, death and then shedding of that hair to be followed by re-growth of a new fresh hair. In hormonal alopecia, new hairs are either very slow to re-grow or fail to grow at all resulting in a hamster getting progressively bald as the older hairs fall out but are not replaced. This is most obvious along the back and sides of the trunk but is often not associated with any itching or pain. The greatest problem is the cosmetic disfigurement.

Treatment: Since it is rare to diagnose the specific hormone involved, treatment is mainly non-specific and aimed at trying to improve the quality of the hair growth in general. Addition of a few drops of cod liver oil to the diet each day may help or indeed of any multivitamin supplement. Anabolic steroid or thyroid hormone supplementation may be useful.

122

Prognosis: The outlook is as for any other older hamster apart from the cosmetic effects.

Homeopathic treatment: Seek expert veterinary homeopathic help.

Skin Mange ***

Causes: Mange refers to infestation of the skin by mites. There are two main types of mites involved. The first is Sarcoptes and is less common but extremely itchy. It is commonly known as the Itch Mite. The second is Demodex, which is much more commonly seen, especially in older individuals. These mites are contracted directly from other affected hamsters and not usually brought into the hamster environment on bedding. The mites may lie dormant in the hamster for several months or years, awaiting a period of immuno-suppression or stress before multiplying and causing disease.

Symptoms: Both species of mite mainly cause skin disease. Sarcoptes tends to be more itchy and mainly affects the head area whereas Demodex often is less itchy or not at all and can affect the whole body although symptoms often begin on the trunk area. Signs include hair loss, thickening of the skin and later on, the appearance of pustules and ulcers as secondary bacterial infections develop. Diagnosis is by recognition of the clinical signs or by using skin scrapes, which can be examined under a microscope for the presence of mites. Sarcoptes can occur at any age while demodex is usually a disease of the older hamster or any hamster suffering immune-suppression.

Treatment: Both of these conditions can be treated with ivermectin which is given every seven-ten days for as long as required (usually 3-5 administrations) and may be administered orally, by injection or applied directly onto the skin. Secondary infection may require treatment by antibiotics such as enrofloxacin while severe pruritus (itchiness) may require short-term corticosteroid treatment. Local treatment of the lesions with antibiotic (FUCIDIN, Leo Laboratories Ltd.) or antibiotic/steroid (FUCIDERM, Leo Laboratories Ltd.) skin creams may also be helpful although these need to be applied sparingly to reduce the levels ingested during grooming.

Prognosis: Sarcoptes is a true primary cause of disease and thus treatment is often curative. Demodex mites, however, are often present in normal hamster skin at low levels but a healthy immune system should not allow them to multiply. The presence of Demodex in large enough numbers to cause disease often points to the existence of other more serious debilitating underlying disease and a full clinical exam is warranted. Prognosis is then dependent on the underlying disease.

Homeopathic treatment: *Sulphur* (if the hamster avoids warmth and if the itch is worsened by warmth) or *Psorinum* (if the hamster desires warmth and covering and is improved by warmth). Many different homeopathic remedies may prove useful, however, depending upon the exact signs shown, so expert homeopathic veterinary help may be needed if these suggestions fail.

Ear Mites/ Ear Mange ***
Causes: The causal agent is one of the mites called Notoedres that live around the ears but can also be present elsewhere on the face and on the feet.

Symptoms: As the mites multiply around the ear region, the hamster becomes allergic to them and an itchy scaling dermatitis develops. The skin will become crusty and darkened. The hamster may show deep injuries around the

124

head region due to self-mutilation.

Treatment: As for all the mite-induced diseases, treatment mainly involves ivermectin administered weekly over several weeks. Repeat skin scrapes need to be taken to prove the infestation has been resolved as treatment may be required for as many as 8-12 weeks. Local treatment of the lesions with antibiotic or steroid-based creams (FUCIDIN or FUCIDERM Leo Laboratories Ltd) may be required to rapidly reduce initial itching. The environment needs to be thoroughly cleaned at the time of each weekly treatment to avoid re-contamination of the hamsters by mites harbouring in the bedding.

Prognosis: The prognosis is good if treatment is given before the self-induced trauma has led to severe skin damage. Since some of these mites can also be harboured by cats as well as by other hamsters, treatment of those in-contact and source animals needs to be considered to prevent recurrence.

The infestation is very contagious and can affect an entire colony when hamsters are kept together.

Homeopathic treatment: As for mange but aromatherapy (essential oils) can also be very useful in treating this condition. Use diluted oils (in, say, olive oil), sparingly, for direct application. *Lavender, Rosemary, Tea Tree*, and *Garlic* oils are all very useful for this type of problem.

Ringworm *** **ZOONOSIS**
Causes: Despite its name, the causal agent is not a worm but a type of fungus (Trichophyton or Microsporum) that grows on the skin, hairs and nails. Poor general health or lowered immune status plus injuries to the skin facilitate the development of ringworm.

Symptoms: As the fungus grows on the skin and hairs, hairs are broken leading to bald areas of skin that expand over time. Any part of the body can be affected and the condition is sometimes itchy. Affected nails become distorted, weakened and eventually slough off. Some types of ringworm can be identified by their ability to fluoresce brightly under an ultra-violet light. However, the best diagnostic test is by laboratory culture of a sample of hair plucked from affected skin to check for fungal growth. This can, however, take several weeks and, where disease is likely, it is safest to start treatment immediately.

Treatment: Oral medication with griseofulvin for at least 4 weeks may be combined with shampooing with povidone-iodine, TAMODINE (Vetark professional) or antifungals such as enilconazole or natamycin. Since the fungus prefers high humidity, plastic enclosed cages should be avoided and ventilation improved.

Prognosis: The clinical prognosis for treated cases is good but many owners will opt for euthanasia of affected individuals due the risk of spread of this disease to humans and other animals. Children appear more susceptible than adults. All treatment should be carried out wearing gloves and affected animals should be isolated from children and other pets until a veterinary surgeon has given the all clear. Fungal spores will also be present in the bedding and the cage furniture so similar precautions need to be taken with these. The cage should not be sited in a bedroom. The cages and cage furniture should be thoroughly cleaned with an effective anti-fungal disinfectant such as ARK-KLENS or TAMODINE-E (Vetark Professional). Once treatment appears successful, it would be wise to dispose of all cages, bedding and cage furniture to prevent any remaining spores causing recurrence. Repeat hair samples need to be tested to prove cure has occurred.

Homeopathic treatment: This condition usually responds well to homeopathy, prescribed by a vet with the appropriate expertise.

Allergic Skin Disease ***

Causes: In common with humans where allergies such as asthma, eczema and hay fever seem to be on the increase, such diseases can also affect hamsters. The allergies are often to bedding or certain components of the diet, but animals can be allergic to almost anything they come into contact with, such as air freshener or carpet cleaners.

Symptoms: Depending upon which part of the body is sensitive to the allergen, symptoms vary from sneezing/eye discharge (hay fever), greasy skin/hair loss/itchy skin (dermatitis, eczema) or difficulty breathing (asthma). Diagnosis is often by removal of the causal agent with a consequent clinical improvement. Re-exposure to this item should result in a recurrence of symptoms.

Treatment: The best treatment is to identify the cause and to remove it without the need for any drugs. Wood-based bedding can be replaced with shredded paper or tissue, while diets with artificial ingredients can be replaced with natural foods such as rice, vegetables and fruits. Any potential airborne agents such as room air fresheners, including the plug-in type, exposure to cigarette smoke and even to plants should be removed and ventilation should be improved.

Prognosis: As long as the offending cause can be identified and removed, the prognosis is generally good.

Homeopathic treatment: *Psorinum* or *Graphites* may be of value, in helping to remove the allergic tendency and to heal skin lesions. Many different homeopathic remedies may prove useful, however, depending upon the exact signs shown, so expert homeopathic veterinary help may be needed if these suggestions fail.

Abscesses ***

Cause: An abscess is an accumulation of pus usually as a result of a bacterial infection. The infection can gain entry into the body via a fight wound or any other injury to the skin such as a result of an accident in the cage, or may begin from within the body such as a dental abscess.

Symptoms: A swelling (the abscess) will be noted which enlarges and may rupture to release smelly thick creamy pus. Some hamsters with abscesses look very unwell while others, even with large abscesses, show no other symptoms of illness.

Treatment: Since the cause is a bacterial infection, antibiotics such as trimethoprim-sulphonamide combination or enrofloxacin will help. The abscess itself may be opened and drained or completely excised under anaesthetic, depending on its position and size. If the abscess is opened and left to drain, it should be cleaned twice daily with an effective and safe antiseptic such as TAMODINE (Vetark Professional) or chlorhexidine (HIBISCRUB SSL). Some thought needs to be given to the cause of the abscess and thus how to prevent recurrence. It may be necessary to keep the hamster in isolation if it is a colony animal and fighting was the cause of the abscess or to move the hamster to a single-story cage if it was the result of a fall. Dentistry will be required for a tooth root abscess.

Prognosis: As long as treatment begins early in the course of the disease, the outlook should be good although antibiotic treatment may need to be continued for quite a while.

Homeopathic treatment: In the acute phase, homeopathic *Hepar sulph.* is invaluable, in helping pain and suppuration.

In the chronic phase, *Silica* can be very useful to promote natural elimination of foreign/purulent material.

Hip or Ventral Gland Disease *

Causes: Syrian hamsters have paired darkened areas of skin covered with coarse hair on their hips called hip glands. These glands are more obvious in the males and especially during times of sexual activity. They become more pronounced in older Syrians because the fur gets thinner as the animal ages. The glands produce an oily secretion which is used to mark territory, to help find a mate and also to mark the female after mating. The glands are present on the tummy of most dwarf hamsters and are called ventral glands. As the hamsters age, these glands may become cancerous but this is uncommon.

Symptoms: Unless the glands have become cancerous, their presence is normal. Should a cancer develop, the gland will enlarge, become raised and ulcerated and bleed.

Treatment: No treatment is required for normal glands. Once the glands have become cancerous, they should be surgically removed with a reasonably wide margin of normal skin. Castration may also be considered as these glands are under hormonal control.

Prognosis: In the rare cases of cancers, surgical removal is usually curative.

Homeopathic treatment: It is worth trying homeopathic *Thuja*, in the early stages, to see if the growth can regress. Seek expert veterinary help in monitoring, however, to ensure that the case is suitable for this strategy.

Diseases Affecting The Digestive System

'Wet Tail' ****

Causes: 'Wet Tail' itself is a specific disease called proliferative ileitis, which does cause the tail area to become wet due to diarrhoea. However, the term 'wet tail' is often used to refer to diarrhoea of any cause and indeed sometimes to include any disease where a wet rear end occurs such as urine leakage. In this book we shall use the term 'wet tail' as specifically referring to proliferative ileitis while other causes of soiling of the rear end will be dealt with under their own titles.

Stress for any reason is a major contributory factor in the development of the condition. 'Wet Tail' is common in newly purchased hamsters of 3-10 weeks of age because stresses such as movement to a pet shop and then sale on to the new owner, poor nutrition, overcrowding, temperature fluctuations and poor levels of hygiene lower the immune system. This allows spread of a bacterial organism called *Lawsonia intracellularis* that is thought to be important in the disease process. Some breeds such as the longhaired varieties and indeed even some strains within these breeds appear more susceptible.

Symptoms: As the name suggests, the major sign seen is severe diarrhoea, causing the tail end of the hamster to become wet. The hamster becomes very quiet, moving very little, sitting in a hunched position and not eating. If treatment is not instigated rapidly, it will soon die. Occasionally, part of the rectum (hind bowel) will be forced out through the anus due to the severe straining and can be seen externally.

Treatment: Emergency treatment needs to be instigated and even then, the outlook is poor. Reversal of dehydration is essential. Isotonic fluids may be administered orally (e.g.

LIQUID LECTADE Pfizer Ltd) but absorption is much more rapid and effective if fluids can be given by injection either under the skin or into the peritoneum by your veterinary surgeon. Drug therapy includes antibiotics such as neomycin or metronidazole orally, enrofloxacin, oxytetracycline or sulphonamides by injection, corticosteroids to reverse shock and multi-vitamins to stimulate the immune system. Nutrition is important to get the bowel working again and to improve the immune system. Forced feeding with liquidised vegetables and rodent pellets can be used on individuals that will not eat voluntarily whilst adding sweeteners such as honey to the normal food may encourage an increased appetite in a recovering hamster. High quality general nursing is also vital and the animal should be kept in a warm quiet environment to reduce further stress. Probiotics such as Avipro (Vetark Professional) may assist in re-establishing a normal healthy bowel flora.

Prognosis: The outlook with this condition is poor and the objective often must be to protect other hamsters in the same house whilst also trying to save the sick individual. Correction of underlying stress factors is vital. Inclusion of antibiotics into the water of in-contact hamsters may help (oxytetracycline, erythromycin). Other hamsters close to the affected individuals should be moved into another uninhabited room of the house but remember that this movement itself can also result in further stress. This illness can spread very quickly.

After handling affected individuals, hands need to be carefully washed and the cages and cage furniture of any dead individuals should either be binned or thoroughly washed and disinfected with a disinfectant such as ARK-KLENS (Vetark Professional). Opt for a stronger pet disinfectant than the one you normally use and leave the cage soaking for a period of three weeks before re-homing another hamster into it. Purchase new hamsters directly from the breeder to reduce stress from multiple environmental changes at a young age. Avoidance of susceptible breeds seems sensible.

Homeopathic treatment: *Merc. corr.* is useful in treating this condition and may eliminate the need for antibiotics that may be detrimental to beneficial bowel flora. Many different homeopathic remedies may prove useful, however, depending upon the exact signs shown, so expert homeopathic veterinary help may be needed if these suggestions fail. A nosode may also be made, under expert veterinary guidance.

Tyzzer's Disease ****
Causes: This disease has a specific organism called *Bacillus piliformis* as a causal agent but, as with 'wet tail', stress seems to play a major role in allowing these organisms to cause disease.

Symptoms: These are very similar to 'wet tail' with severe diarrhoea and dullness often leading to rapid death within a day, despite even the most intensive treatment. The diagnosis can only be confirmed on post mortem where the causal organism may be found on samples taken from the liver. The disease usually affects stressed young individuals.

Treatment: This is the same as for 'wet tail' including immediate rehydration, antibiotics, probiotics and intensive nursing in a warm quiet environment.

Prognosis: Unfortunately, most cases die despite intensive treatment and the real objective is often to prevent spread of the disease to in-contacts. As for 'wet tail', inclusion of antibiotics into the drinking water may help to control the spread e.g. oxytetracycline. All cages and cage furniture should be thoroughly cleaned with a disinfectant such as ARK-KLENS (Vetark Professional). Spores from the causal organism survive for up to a year in contaminated bedding, soil and food so it would be wise to discard all current items and start afresh with new equipment. It is preferable to use pre-packed foods to avoid contamination. Hay or straw used as bedding may also be contaminated with faeces from wild rodents that can carry and spread the disease.

Homeopathic treatment: As for 'wet tail', since homeopathy selects remedies on the basis of signs shown by each animal, not by disease name. A nosode could prove useful in treating chronic cases or, as with all infective diseases, to help prevent spread to other individuals (homeoprophylaxis). Expert homeopathic veterinary guidance is needed for this specialist application of homeopathy.

Antibiotic-Induced diarrhoea ****

Causes: The normal intestine of hamsters (and indeed of all mammals) maintains a delicate normal ecosystem of micro-organisms. These organisms are important in helping digestion of food, production of vitamins and prevention of entry to the body by disease-causing organisms by competing with them for space. Administration of some types of antibiotics can disrupt this normal ecosystem by killing off some of these 'good' bacteria and result in 'bad' bacteria multiplying in the bowel and causing disease. Examples of such dangerous antibiotics include orally administered erythromycin, penicillin, lincomycin, cephalosporin and streptomycin.

Symptoms: The commonest symptom is severe diarrhoea that may often lead to a rapid death from the multiplication of 'bad' bacteria such as Clostridia spp. and the poisons (enterotoxins) that they produce.

Treatment: Cease administration of the unsuitable antibiotic immediately. Use a probiotic (source of 'good' live bacteria) to try to re-establish a normal bowel flora of beneficial bacteria.

133

Proprietary brands such as AVIPRO (Vetark Professional) are available or, alternatively, live natural yoghurt can be used as a probiotic. The potential disadvantage of using yoghurt is that the milk proteins and sugars may, in themselves, increase the diarrhoea. The fluid and nursing therapy discussed for 'wet tail' also apply.

Prognosis: Individual cases carry a poor prognosis and thus prevention is the key. Certain antibiotics such as penicillin and lincomycin should be avoided unless laboratory testing shows there to be no alternative. Routine probiotic usage should always accompany treatment with any antibiotic that may cause this disease.

Homeopathic treatment: In all animals, antibiotic usage brings the risk of bowel disturbance. The mechanism is the destruction of beneficial commensal bacteria in the bowel. This can become chronic and can be very serious in some cases. Homeopathic *Nux vomica 30c* or homeopathic *Aloe 30c* may help, but expert veterinary homeopathic help is advised.

Diet-Induced Diarrhoea **
Causes: As with all species, digestion of foods result from enzymes produced in the bowel itself and also by organisms that live in the bowel. Eating a regular consistent diet encourages the development of the optimum enzymes and organisms. Whenever the diet is suddenly changed or foods are offered that have gone bad, there is a risk that the new food item may not be properly digested by current bowel enzymes or by current bowel organisms. This can result in diarrhoea.

Symptoms: The hamster will initially not look sick but will show mild to severe diarrhoea. As the condition worsens, the hamster will begin to look sick and dull and dehydrated as for other types of diarrhoea.

Treatment: Remove all new foods that have been recently introduced. Check all foods offered to ensure they are fresh and have not become mouldy. Clean the cage to remove all old stored foods that may have gone bad and remember to pay extra attention to the corners of the cage where foods are often stored. Check the water bottles to ensure they are not the source of the problem and clean them thoroughly in boiling water before refilling with cold water. Offer fresh dry food to physically dry up the diarrhoea within the hamster. Additional therapy with arrowroot in the form of biscuits or powder may help. Kaolin/pectin mixtures such as Kaogel V (Pharmacia & Upjohn Animal Health Ltd) help to bind any poisons produced within the gut and to thicken the stools and may be helpful. If the hamster appears dehydrated, isotonic electrolyte fluids are indicated. Probiotics such as Avipro (Vetark Professional) may assist in re-establishing a normal healthy bowel flora.

Prognosis: The prognosis is as for all diarrhoeas of hamsters and must be guarded. Early intervention is the key to successful treatment.

Homeopathic treatment: The use of *probiotics* may help the situation, by restoring compromised bacterial balance in the bowel. Homeopathic *Nux vomica* or *Natrum carb.* may help the patient to regain health and normal bowel function.

If the diarrhoea is a result of 'spoiled' food, homeopathic *Arsenicum album* is usually the medicine of choice but *Nux vomica* may also help. Consult a homeopathic veterinary surgeon for help with this, as it is a potentially serious condition.

Intestinal Parasites ** ZOONOSIS**
Causes: There are several parasite worms that can infest the intestines of hamsters. A tapeworm called *Hymenolepis nana*

is common and is transmissible to man (zoonosis). *Syphacia obvelata* is a pinworm that is also common. Several types of protozoa have been recorded in hamsters such as Cryptosporidium, Balantidium and Giardia. They are also transmissible to man.

Symptoms: Tapeworm infestation often has no symptoms. When there are problems, these can include diarrhoea and weight loss. Pinworm infestation rarely shows any symptoms. Severe infestation can cause diarrhoea and abdominal swelling. None of the protozoa seem to cause disease in hamsters.

Treatment: Tapeworm infestation can be treated with praziquantal (DRONCIT Bayer Ltd). Pinworms can be treated with piperazine, fenbendazole or ivermectin. Giardia infestation can be treated with fenbendazole at a higher dose than is used for pinworm treatment.

Prognosis: None of these parasitic diseases are of major consequence in their own right. However, because of the risk of spread by several of them to humans, regular monitoring and treatment is advisable.

Homeopathic treatment: Seek expert veterinary homeopathic help if you wish to pursue this route.

Yersinia*** ZOONOSIS
Causes: This is a specific disease caused by a bacterium called *Yersinia pseudotuberculosis*. Sources can either be other infected hamsters or the faeces of wild birds or rodents.

Symptoms: The organism lives in the various organs of the abdomen and symptoms include weight loss, diarrhoea and generally looking unwell. In some cases of severe disease, the first signs seen are dead hamsters. The diagnosis is made by a veterinary post mortem where samples taken from the hamster will show up the causal organism.

Treatment: Due to the risks of spread of this organism to humans, treatment is not advisable. Affected individuals should be humanely euthanased and all cages and cage furniture destroyed or thoroughly disinfected with an effective disinfectant such as ARK-KLENS (Vetark Professional). Access to wild birds and rodents should be prevented. Probiotics such as Avipro (Vetark Professional) may assist in re-establishing a normal healthy bowel flora.

Homeopathic treatment: Homeopathic treatment may be of benefit in prevention of spread, possibly by use of nosodes (seek expert veterinary homeopathic help for this). Treatment of affected animals is risky, by virtue of the danger of infection to humans. It is only advisable with expert veterinary homeopathic guidance.

Intussusception ****
Causes: Intussusception refers to a condition where a section of intestine telescopes into itself resulting in either partial or total blockage of the bowel. It may result due to any cause of straining such as any of the diarrhoeas detailed above or from constipation.

Symptoms: These hamsters look extremely dull and sick and are in great pain. There is usually a bloody discharge from the rectum or diarrhoea. The hamster rapidly dehydrates and dies.

Treatment: Since the main problem is a twisted bowel, only immediate surgery would be curative but this is rarely successful. Euthanasia may be the kindest option.

Prognosis: Very poor, either with or without surgery. Early treatment of diarrhoeas and constipation to prevent the condition is the best approach.

Homeopathic treatment: *Nux vomica* has been known to help early cases, before the processes have become advanced.

Prolapsed Rectum****

Causes: This is very similar to intussusception but instead of the telescoped part of the bowel being far up in the abdomen, it is the rectum or final part of the bowel that twists into itself. This results in a fleshy piece of bowel protruding from the anus. Again, the primary cause is straining due to any cause.

Symptoms: As described, a portion of the rectum will be seen protruding from the anus. These hamsters look very unwell and rapidly deteriorate.

Treatment: Surgery is possible if the condition is caught early before the exposed rectum has had time to dry out or become damaged. Surgery may either involve replacing the prolapsed section of bowel under general anaesthesia followed by applying a purse-string suture to the anus to prevent recurrence or the total removal of the prolapsed section if it has been too badly damaged to salvage. Antibiotics and fluids need to be administered and postoperative painkillers should be used. The primary cause of straining also needs to be addressed.

Prognosis: The outlook is still guarded but is better than for an intussusception of the small bowel. The underlying cause of the problem must be elucidated to prevent future recurrence.

Homeopathic treatment: *Ruta* and *Æsculus* can help in replacement of such lesions and can help to lessen the tendency to repeat incidents.

Constipation***
Causes: This is a build up of solid dry material that blocks the bowel. The main causes are either the ingestion of indigestible material such as some types of bedding fibres or insufficient fluid intake. Obesity and inadequate exercise predispose to constipation.

Symptoms: Since the problem is an obstruction of the bowel, the signs are initially straining without any faeces being produced as the hamster tries to free the blockage. As the condition worsens, the bowel becomes damaged and the hamster will show pain and walk with an arched back. The tummy will begin to swell up as further faeces accumulate in the bowel. It is important to remember that there are other causes of straining apart from constipation. These include urinary disease, tumours around the rear end, diarrhoea itself or uterine disease.

Treatment: Medical treatment involves the use of one of many available types of laxative. Two drops of either liquid paraffin or lactulose can be given four times daily. Mild cases can be given natural laxatives such as lettuce or dandelion or a pinch of Epsom salts can be added to the drinking water. The bedding material should be switched and consideration needs to be given to the diet to prevent recurrence. Exercise should be encouraged.

Prognosis: The outlook is favourable in mild or early cases but once the condition has progressed or secondary signs such as intussusception or rectal prolapse are present, then treatment is often hopeless.

Homeopathic treatment: *Nux vomica* is the first-aid treatment of choice, in this condition. Many different homeopathic remedies may prove useful, however, depending upon the exact signs shown, so expert homeopathic veterinary help may be needed if these suggestions fail.

Diseases Affecting the Respiratory and Cardiovascular System

Aspergillosis***
Causes: Aspergillosis is caused by one of a number of fungi belonging to the aspergillus family, the commonest being *Aspergillus fumigatus*. Fungal spores are airborne and very common, resulting in fungal growth as moulds on decaying vegetable matter or urine/faeces in cages. As the fungus multiplies, large numbers of spores are released that can be inhaled by animals in close proximity, resulting in disease. Fungal growth is favoured in warm moist environments and especially in the presence of high amounts of urine.

Symptoms: The main symptoms shown are respiratory problems with wheezing and difficulty breathing. These signs may develop slowly over several days as a result of growth of a fungal mass called an aspergilloma in the lungs or airways. Affected hamsters will sit in a hunched position, with an arched back, as this makes breathing easier. They become very lethargic, staying in one part of the cage and not even moving to get food and water. It is also possible to see an acute asthmatic-type reaction as a result of a severe allergic reaction to the inhaled spores. Some hamsters may show itchy skin or diarrhoea, also as a result of allergies to the inhaled spores. Specific diagnosis comes after a complete post mortem when histopathology and fungal culture will demonstrate the presence of aspergillus in lung tissue.

Treatment: Unfortunately, once a hamster has Aspergillosis, there is little chance of cure as the disease progresses rapidly and the response to treatment is poor. In other animals such as parrots where the disease is common, anti-fungal drugs such as ketoconazole (NIZORAL Squibb) or amphotericin B (FUNGIZONE Squibb) are used but, even then, the response to treatment is poor. The most important aspect of treatment is prevention of further infection for other hamsters. Any factor known to favour growth of the fungus should be removed. The fungus requires an organic base on which to multiply such as decomposing vegetable matter or wet shavings. Fresh foods should be provided in only small pieces to encourage total consumption. Uneaten food or dampened, soiled bedding should be removed daily. Since urine strongly encourages growth, cage hygiene is very important. Hamsters with increased urine output such as those with diabetes or kidney failure need to be especially carefully monitored.

Treatment with antibiotics will kill some normal bacteria in the body that act as a natural defence mechanism to the growth of fungi such as aspergillus and thus may encourage the disease. Antibiotic treatment should always be matched with increased cage hygiene. Stress, old age, pregnancy, poor nutrition or inter-current disease also reduce the natural immune system of the body and increase the risks of fungal disease.

Since the fungal spores are airborne, hamsters sharing the same cage as well as those in other cages sharing the same airspace are at risk of also contracting aspergillosis. All cages should be thoroughly cleaned using a disinfectant with anti-fungal properties such as Tamodine E (Vetark Professional). Extra attention should be paid to those areas where the hamster urinates, where water bottles drip and where food is stored. Such cleaning should continue to be carried out on a weekly basis.

Prognosis: The outlook for affected hamsters is poor. However, the outlook for the in-contacts is much better because cage hygiene is very successful at controlling the growth and pathogenicity of the fungus.

Aspergillosis as a disease of hamsters has become topical recently in the hamster press and is quoted as being a common and important cause of sudden and unexplained deaths in hamsters. However, laboratory-proven cases appear to be few, although this may be due to the financial cost involved in definitive diagnosis. Either way, however, an understanding of the life cycle of the causal agent will hopefully lead to a reduction in the true incidence as awareness and thus cage hygiene improves.

Homeopathic treatment: Many cases have responded, in all species, to homeopathic treatment. It is a field for expert homeopathic veterinary help, however, since it is a very complex and potentially serious disease.

Asthma/ Hay Fever ***
Causes: As for humans, hamsters may develop allergies to multitudes of allergens. These may include dietary ingredients or additives, bedding materials, cage cleaners, and fumes such as room air fresheners, including the plug-in type, cigarette smoke and even the owner's deodorants

Symptoms: Asthma (severe wheezy breathing) results when the main reaction is in the windpipe and lungs whilst hay fever with runny itchy eyes and a runny nose with sneezing occur when it is the eyes that are most affected. Affected hamsters may also show skin signs as described in the section on allergic skin disease.

Treatment: The most effective treatment is to remove the cause, which should result in complete resolution of the signs.

All potential allergens should be methodically eliminated until symptoms improve. Deliberate re-exposure to the suspected agent can be used to prove for certain its role in the disease. If secondary infection has resulted, then the short-term use of antibiotics such as enrofloxacin may be required. Treatment with bronchodilators or corticosteroids such as Betsolan Soluble (Fort Dodge Animal Health Ltd) may be necessary for rapid initial alleviation of symptoms.

Prognosis: If the offending items can be identified and removed, then the outlook should be good. Since there may be a familial link in the disease as in humans, affected individuals and the siblings should not be used for breeding.

Homeopathic treatment: *Pulsatilla*, *Euphrasia*, *Aconite* or *Sabadilla* may be beneficial, depending upon presenting signs. Many different homeopathic remedies may prove useful, however, depending upon the exact signs shown, so expert homeopathic veterinary help may be needed if these suggestions fail.

'Colds' ** ZOONOSIS

Causes: As is the case for humans, there are a myriad of factors involved in respiratory infections or 'colds'. Hamsters can contract many of the bacteria and viruses that cause the human common cold. Very young, very old, pregnant or otherwise unwell individuals are more at risk. Stress factors such as extremes of temperature, poor quality bedding or poor nutrition also lower the immune system and increase susceptibility to disease. Bacteria such as Streptococcus spp. are commonly implicated. Many healthy hamsters carry *Pasteurella pneumotropica* without clinical signs becoming evident until periods of stress.

Symptoms: Because of their small size, these 'colds' are more dangerous for the hamster than for their owner. Affected hamsters look unwell and dull and sit in a hunched position. They demonstrate a fever by shivering and appearing cold. Runny eyes and noses are combined with sneezing and wheezing.

Treatment: A combination of drug therapy with intensive nursing care is vital to the success of treatment. Sick hamsters must be kept quiet and warm. Palatable foods should be offered to encourage them to eat while fluid therapy is often necessary. Offering a mixture of lukewarm milk and water with a little added honey may encourage drinking. Human mentholated ointments will ease laboured breathing. The initial upper respiratory disease can become complicated by secondary infection with bacteria leading to pneumonia. Antibiotics such as enrofloxacin, marbofloxacin, oxytetracycline, chloramphenicol or potentiated sulphonamides are useful in these situations.

Prognosis: If treatment is given early and aggressively, then most animals respond. Unfortunately, secondary bacterial infection often develops with abscesses in other parts of the body such as the middle ear leading to head tilts. These are much harder to treat successfully. Owners or visitors with colds need to be kept away to prevent further organisms being contracted.

Homeopathic treatment: *Pulsatilla* is likely to be helpful. Many different homeopathic remedies may prove useful, however, depending upon the exact signs shown, so expert homeopathic veterinary help may be needed if these suggestions fail.

Herbal treatment: Echinacea can be given to help boost the immune system, although this should not be given in the long term.

Age-Related Respiratory Disease **

Causes: As hamsters age, many factors can result in loss of respiratory function. These include the development of lung tumours, heart disease and chronic bronchitis.

Symptoms: As well as the general slowing down seen with ageing, these affected hamsters show rapid exhaustion and collapse even after very mild exercise. A bluish tinge to the feet and ear tips where this used to be pink demonstrates low blood oxygen level.

Treatment: There is often very little by way of specific treatment that can be given. Reducing the exercise requirement by moving the hamsters to single level cages and shortening or even elimination of play and exercise in wheels or balls may help. Reduction of inhaled irritants such as ammonia should be achieved by strict cage hygiene and consideration should be given to the involvement of aspergillosis in the clinical picture. Where secondary infection is present, use of antibiotics such as enrofloxacin may be helpful, as may the use of corticosteroids or bronchodilators where chronic bronchitis is severe.

Prognosis: The prognosis depends on the primary cause of the breathing difficulties. However, due to the short life expectancy of hamsters and the fact that these diseases are age-related, the long-term outlook is not good.

Homeopathic treatment: *Carbo veg.* or *Arsenicum album* may help. Homeopathic preparations of *Digitalis*, in the 12c potency or higher, are quite safe and can often help heart-related conditions. If there is heart-related lung congestion, then *Spongia* may help. Many different homeopathic remedies may prove useful, however, depending upon the exact signs shown, so expert homeopathic veterinary help may be needed if these suggestions fail. For example, the powerful medicines *Tub. bov.* or *Carcinosin* may be required, which should not be given except under expert homeopathic veterinary guidance.

Heart Failure ***

Causes: Heart failure may result from either clots developing with the heart itself or from weakening of the heart muscle. Both of these conditions are age-related and usually are seen in hamsters over 18 months of age.

Symptoms: As the heart fails, less blood is being pumped around the body and the hamster will become weak and out of breath. 'Fainting' may occur with exercise such as during play in an exercise wheel. A bluish tinge will appear over the abdomen and legs where the animal had previously had a healthy pink colouration. Sudden death with no warning signs may often be the first evidence of the problem.

Treatment: Since this is an age-related disease, treatment is often unrewarding. Treatment with cardiac drugs used in other species may help including digoxin, frusemide and ACE-inhibitors. The activity level of the hamster should be reduced to lessen the demands on the failing heart. The exercise wheel may be removed and the hamster placed in a single-level cage. Handling should be reduced.

Prognosis: The prognosis for severe heart disease in older hamsters is not good. Even with treatment, affected individuals rarely survive longer than 1-3 weeks. The prognosis for younger individuals is much better.

Homeopathic treatment: Since balancing of heart function is so complex, you are advised to seek expert veterinary homeopathic help. Many homeopathic medicines have an important role to play in heart treatment.

Diseases affecting the Urinary and Reproductive System

Bladder Stones ***
Causes: Bladder stones (uroliths) are the result of crystals progressively joining together in the bladder to form a small stone or stones. Hamster urine is often naturally rich in crystals and any low-grade urinary infection tends to encourage stone development. The use of shavings or chippings as a flooring/ bedding material is often implicated because the high moisture absorbency tends to lower the humidity of the cage. This results in increased fluid losses via the skin and exhaled air with a resultant reduction of fluids available for urine production. A smaller volume of a more concentrated urine is produced that is more conducive to stone development.

Symptoms: The stones irritate the lining of the bladder resulting in further infection and cystitis. Tiny drops of bloody urine may leak from the hamster. Urination will be frequent but of small volume. The hamster will show pain, especially when urinating and begin to look unwell. Your veterinary surgeon may be able to palpate the stones by gently feeling the abdomen whilst other cases may only be diagnosed by radiography or surgery.

Treatment: Since the clinical signs result from irritation by the physical presence of stones within the bladder, the only cure is surgical removal of the offending stones. This is delicate and tricky surgery but is often successful with the hamster recovering well afterwards. Antibiotics such as enrofloxacin may be used to treat any secondary bacterial cystitis.

Prognosis: Provided the hamster comes through the operation, the condition need not be terminal but stones tend to recur with a requirement for repeat surgeries. Offering dandelion leaves that have a diuretic effect may encourage increased urine production and thus more regular flushing of the bladder with dilution of urine crystals. A similar effect may result from the addition of low levels of table salt to the water or food. Addition of a little fruit juice to salted water may improve palatability to increase consumption. Replacement of some of the dry rodent mix by fresh vegetables and some soaked foods will increase the fluid intake component via the food. Extra vitamin C (ascorbic acid) added to the food may assist by acidifying the urine and thus reducing crystallisation of some types of stone materials.

Homeopathic treatment: The stones may dissolve slowly, under the influence of homeopathic *Berberis*. Seek veterinary help with monitoring. This remedy, along with *Lycopodium*, can usually prevent the reformation of stones after surgery.

Chronic Kidney Failure **
Causes: Progressive loss of kidney function leading to chronic kidney failure is thought to be the principal cause of death in older hamsters. This is often a result of an ageing phenomenon called amyloidosis that has been described in 88% of hamsters over 18 months of age. Females seem to develop the problem earlier in life and be more severely affected than males. Chronic kidney failure may also follow a prior episode of heat stroke, especially if fluids were not administered soon enough after the onset of problems.

Symptoms: As an adaptation to living in arid environments, hamster kidneys are capable of producing extremely concentrated urine to conserve water. Thus hamster urine is normally thick and creamy in appearance. A normal hamster produces 5-8ml urine per 24-hour period. With chronic kidney failure, the ability to produce concentrated urine is lost resulting in the production of larger volumes of more dilute urine and thus requiring the hamster to drink more water.

As the condition worsens, despite the larger volumes of urine, waste products fail to be eliminated from the body. The resultant build-up of toxins in the body cause the hamster to look unwell showing sticky eyes, losing weight and poor hair coat.

Treatment: As this is often an age-related disease, total cure may not be possible. Occasionally infections may be involved and the use of antibiotics such as enrofloxacin can be useful. Use of anabolic steroids may delay the loss of body muscle protein mass and thus reduce the demands on the failing kidney. Since it is an accumulation of nitrogenous waste from the digestion of proteins that is mainly responsible for the symptoms of kidney failure, then a dietary reduction of protein intake should be beneficial. Puffed rice cereal or cooked rice increases the carbohydrate component of the diet and reduces the protein level. Additional B-vitamins may also help.

Prognosis: The prognosis for individual cases with chronic kidney failure is poor. Many cases progress to develop secondary disease such as demodectic mange due to immune suppression. Consideration needs to be given to the higher risks from aspergillosis and ammonia-induced respiratory disease due to the large amounts of urine passed.

Homeopathic treatment: Seek expert veterinary homeopathic help with this but it is acceptable to commence treatment with *Mercurius solubilis*, pending an appointment.

Mastitis ***
Causes: Mastitis refers to inflammation and infection of the mammary glands often by streptococci bacteria. This is likely to happen when the mammary glands are swollen with milk, usually 7-10 days after giving birth. The young will often die by cannibalism or because the mother refuses to nurse due to

the resultant discomfort.

Symptoms: One or all of the mammary glands will be enlarged, hot and tender and may show a blood coloured discharge instead of milk. The mother hamster will look sick and unwell.

Treatment: Since bacteria are often involved as either primary or secondary causes of the mastitis, antibiotic therapy is indicated. Any broad-spectrum antibiotic should help such as enrofloxacin. Bathing and massage of the affected gland with a warm compress will help to relieve discomfort and remove some of the infected discharge. Anti-inflammatories such as meloxicam reduce pain and swelling and encourage eating.

Prognosis: The prognosis for the babies is poor. They are either cannibalised by the suffering, stressed mother or prevented from suckling because nursing is so painful. If treatment is started rapidly and aggressively, the outlook for the dam is better but it would be wise not to use her for breeding again.

Homeopathic treatment: Urgent expert veterinary homeopathic help is advisable in such cases but a combination of *Belladonna, Bryonia* and *Urtica*, perhaps with *Sepia* if there is a tendency to cannibalisation, can often help.

Uterine Infections ***
Causes: Bacterial infections of the uterus (called pyometra) may be secondary to spread from urinary or respiratory infections or due to one of a range of hormonal imbalances.

Symptoms: The uterus fills with pus causing the tummy to enlarge. Pus may spill out of the uterus via the cervix leading to a sticky creamy vaginal discharge. As the condition progresses, the hamster will start to look unwell with sticky eyes. It will lose weight and feel bony despite the swollen abdomen.

Treatment: Initial treatment is directed at the infection itself with antibiotics such as enrofloxacin or the sulphonamides but cure is achieved by surgery when the entire uterus and ovaries are removed (ovariohysterectomy).

Prognosis: Medical treatment alone is unlikely to resolve the problem but provided the animal comes through surgery, the prognosis is good. It is important to note that the normal female hamster will produce a thick vaginal discharge around the second day of each oestrous cycle. This discharge should not be interpreted as a sign of disease and will disappear a day or two later.

Homeopathic treatment: In the earlier stages, the need for surgery or antibiotics can often be averted, through expert homeopathic veterinary input.

Subfertility **

Causes: Subfertility refers to a reduced ability to breed in males or females. There are several different aspects that need to be considered as contributory factors. Physical factors such as obesity, old age and ovarian cysts are important. Behavioural factors include the relative amounts of daylight to darkness given as well as to social ranking in colony animals. Poor quality diet may also be involved with deficiencies of specific vitamins and minerals being relevant. Attempts at breeding between different breeds of hamster can result in genetic defects that can reduce fertility and viability of the young that are born.

Symptoms: Repeated attempts at breeding with poor or no success or apparently successful breeding only to find the female coming back into season at odd intervals.

Treatment: Any specific health problems identified on physical examination need to be addressed. Overweight individuals need to lose weight and exercise should be encouraged. The hours of daylight exposure can be altered artificially to make the animals think they are approaching springtime and thus entering the breeding season. Switching partners after breeding has failed repeatedly may help to overcome any genetic incompatibility between a pairing. Colony pairs should be separated into different tanks to reduce suppression of breeding in subservient pairs by their more dominant housemates.

Prognosis: A careful and systematic approach to the problem will often identify the causal factors contributing to the problems. Combined with patience and repeated attempts at breeding, this approach is most likely to be successful.

Homeopathic treatment: A low potency of *Pulsatilla* (e.g. 6x) may help. If it fails, seek expert homeopathic veterinary assistance.

Ovarian Cysts ***
Causes: In a non-breeding female, normal ovarian activity may result in cysts developing on the ovaries.

Symptoms: These cysts are hormonally active and result in stimulation of the lining of the uterus, often leading to uterine infections (see relevant section on pyometra). The cysts themselves can become quite large and result in a swollen abdomen. Cysts are often present on both ovaries simultaneously.

Treatment: The cysts themselves can be treated by hormone injections but this treatment carries a high risk.

152

Alternatively, they can be drained via a needle inserted through the abdominal wall by your veterinary surgeon although they may recur later. The best approach for long-term cure is surgical removal of the ovaries and uterus (ovariohysterectomy). Secondary uterine infections are treated as described in the relevant section.

Prognosis: Affected individuals are no longer of use as breeding animals but provided they survive surgery, their long-term prognosis is good.

Homeopathic treatment: Homeopathic *Apis mellifica* will help many cases. If it fails, seek expert homeopathic veterinary assistance.

Pregnancy Toxaemia ***
Causes: Overweight individuals in either late pregnancy or soon after giving birth may suddenly release fat from fat reserves in the body into the blood stream if they do not eat for a few days. This fat may then be deposited in excess amounts in the liver leading to liver failure and kidney problems.

Symptoms: Affected animals will become dull and hunched. They stop eating and often have a rapid and shallow breathing. If untreated, they become progressively more lethargic until they go into a coma and die.

Treatment: It is very important to encourage these animals to eat. Force-feeding of liquidised diets or offering favourite foods helps to stimulate metabolism and reverse the pathological changes to the liver. Fluid therapy will reduce kidney damage and help to rid the body of toxins. Fluids may be administered by your veterinary surgeon injecting fluids into the peritoneum or by oral administration of isotonic electrolytes. Multi-vitamins injected or administered orally will help to further stimulate metabolism.

Prognosis: If the condition is spotted early, affected individuals can be saved but the litter is usually lost, whether it is unborn or newborn. Correct nutrition for pregnant individuals is important to reduce the occurrence of this condition.

Homeopathic treatment: In view of the potential seriousness of this problem, expert homeopathic veterinary help should be sought. *Lycopodium* may help in the interim, as a first aid measure.

Cancers

Cancers in General ***
Causes: Cancers (also called tumours or growths) are groups of cells within the body that multiply and grow outside the normal control mechanisms of the body. These growths are classed as more or less malignant depending on the importance to life of the tissue they affect, their rate of growth and whether they tend to seed out into other parts of the body as secondary tumours. Nobody really understands the cause of cancers but lowered immunity as the body ages is an important factor. Thus the risk from cancer rises with age. One specific type of cancer (trichoepithelioma) has been shown to be caused by a virus and is dealt with in the next section.

Symptoms: The commonest finding is a lump somewhere on the body that grows over time. Other specific symptoms are dependent upon where in the body the cancer is present. Tumours of the adrenal glands are reported to occur in as many as 50% of hamsters over 2 years of age. These release hormones that result in skin thinning and hair-loss and often the secondary development of demodectic mange.

154

Treatment: There are many different modalities of treatment for cancer with varying success rates. It is important that any suspicious lumps are examined as soon as possible by your veterinary surgeon. Optimum results follow treatment carried out early in the disease process before the cancer has an opportunity to spread. Some benign tumours that are deemed to be low risk and non-painful may just be monitored for malignant change and left untreated initially. Chemotherapy and radiotherapy are not commonly used in hamsters for technical and financial reasons but could be useful in some cases.

Homeopathic treatment: Cancers can respond to homeopathic medication, in some cases. It is recommended that this be provided by a veterinary surgeon with the appropriate expertise.

'Tumours' of the Rear End (Testicles!)

This section is included not because it is a real disease but because worried owners often present hamsters to their vet 'afflicted' with this condition. Young male hamsters have two testicles that can be present within the abdomen or in the scrotum below the tail. Either way, these testicles are initailly small and may not even be noticed by owners. As the hamster reaches puberty (two to four months) and especially in the springtime, these testicles start to grow and can become quite large and easily visible from a distance. Be assured that this is quite normal and testicular cancer at this young age is very unusual. However, if you are still concerned, it is always worth checking out your individual animal with your vet.

Polyomavirus Infection: Trichoepithelioma/ Transmissible Lymphoma **

Causes: The causal agent is a virus called Hamster Polyomavirus. As well as causing these skin tumours of the hair follicles, it has also been shown to cause transmissible lymphoma, a contagious lymphoid cancer. The virus is found in infected hamster urine and is extremely contagious via such contaminated urine. It can be spread directly animal to animal or indirectly via contaminated hands or bedding, food utensils and cages that have been improperly disinfected. Although pups are not infected in the womb, they can pick up the virus shortly after birth from an infected mother.

Symptoms: Trichoepitheliomas appear as pink rounded masses, commonly on the haired skin of the face, neck, trunk and feet. There are often many growths present on each hamster with more appearing even after some have been surgically removed. Severe outbreaks can happen in colony situations. Diagnosis of trichoepithelioma by a laboratory is accepted as definite proof of the presence of the virus even without virus isolation itself. Transmissible lymphoma involves tumour development in lymph nodes anywhere in the body with possible spread to several other organs such as the liver, kidneys or thymus. Affected hamsters lose weight and the tumours can often be felt as lumps in their tummies. Transmissible lymphoma can result in epizootics with attack rates as high as 80% within a 4-30 week period. This is almost diagnostic for the viral disease since lymphomas normally occur at a low incidence in hamsters and even then mainly in aged individuals. Definitive diagnosis of both versions of the viral disease is via laboratory tests on samples of affected tissue.

Treatment: Individual trichoepithelioma lesions can be surgically removed but new lesions are likely to develop since the virus will still be present in the body. Chemotherapy, as used in humans for lymphoma, could be attempted in hamsters with transmissible lymphoma but is only likely to prolong life at best and not to affect a cure. There is no known cure for the disease.

Prognosis: This disease can cause devastating outbreaks resulting in loss of complete colonies. Once the virus gets established in a unit, it cannot be effectively eliminated without slaughter of the entire population and thorough decontamination of the premises. Even under these circumstances, repeated outbreaks have been known to occur, possibly because of the resistance of the virus to environmental decontamination and the long incubation period from contact with the virus to the development of disease (4-18 months). This long incubation period combined with the widespread nature of the virus and its ease of spread make this disease one of the greatest threats to the hamster industry since hamsters first arrived in the UK soon after the Second World War.

Homeopathic Treatment: This disease lends itself to the technique of Nosode preparation and administration, in order to slow or to prevent spread. There are also treatment possibilities in the early stages, for affected hamsters. Expert homeopathic veterinary help is essential from the outset.

Alfie was approximately 8 months old when he arrived at his rescue home. He had what appeared to be a wart like growth in the corner of his right eye and a slightly smaller one his bottom left eyelid, although neither appeared to bother him. These were initially treated with Tiacil (gentamicin) eye drops to prevent infection of the masses. Two months later the mass on the right lower eyelid had regressed to being a smaller inactive firm white nodule. However, the mass on the left eyelid was bigger (5mm) and looked more aggressive, plus a new red mass had appeared in the skin on his chin.

month later both masses were adjudged to be slightly bigger. Six weeks later both had doubled in size and were surgically removed. At the time of surgery a further two masses were found and also removed. All the wounds healed well but Alfie had an episode of non-pruritic hair loss, which responded well to topical Ivomec. Histopathology performed on the masses showed them to be consistent with trichoepitheliomas. Over the next 8 months Alfie underwent a further two operations to remove additional masses. During this time his teeth started to grow abnormally, requiring regular trimming. Alfie was 2 years old when he died.

Diseases Affecting the Limbs

Fractured Bones ****

Causes: Due to their small size, hamster bones are obviously very light and easily broken (fractured). Such accidents may happen while the hamster is alone in its cage from falling off a ladder or from an upper level of a multi-storey cage or they could even get their legs trapped in exercise wheels. Old age or dietary deficiency of calcium (such as from a diet high in sunflower seeds) may result in weakened bones (osteoporosis) and make fractures more likely. Accidents during play with owners, especially young children who may handle them too roughly or drop the hamster, can also result in fractures. Hamsters have poor vision and depth perception and will walk over the edge of a table if they are left unattended on high surfaces.

Symptoms: The commonest bone to be broken is the lower part of the tibia in the hind leg. The hamster will drag the affected leg and find it difficult to climb. The leg may be bent at an odd angle at the point of fracture and will be floppy and useless below this point. Whereas other small mammals would limp on 3 legs following a fracture, hamsters continue their normal activity on 4 legs. This exercise often leads to bone fragments penetrating the skin. Such 'normal' activity is often incorrectly interpreted by owners as implying that the animal is not experiencing pain. This is not correct and it is simply an acceptance by a wild animal that it must get on with life or else it will die of starvation or predation. If the bones of the spine are fractured, the hamster may be totally paralysed in both hind legs and be incontinent.

Treatment: Suspected fractures are an emergency and veterinary help should be sought immediately. Handle the hamster as little as possible to reduce further damage with sharp broken ends of bones penetrating through the skin resulting in further pain and infection.

Unfortunately, due to their large body size in relation to their small legs and feet plus their high levels of activity, surgical repair of fractures is not always as successful as for other species. However, fractured long bones of the limb may be repairable using a bone pin if the break point is near the centre of the bone. Should a cast or splint be necessary, the lower and upper incisors will need to be trimmed every 3-4 days to prevent the hamster chewing it off. Fluids (e.g. Lectade), painkillers (e.g. meloxicam) and antibiotics (e.g. enrofloxacin) may need to be administered pre-operatively to reduce signs of shock.

Should the fracture be unsuitable for surgical repair, amputation of the limb may be considered. Many hamsters do well on three legs. In the case of broken backs, the damage to the spinal cord is usually permanent and these animals may need to be euthanased on humane grounds.

There are cases where surgical repair of fractures is not possible because either the nature or position of the break is unsuitable for pinning or the anaesthetic risk is felt to be too high. Acceptable levels of natural repair may result in some cases with total cage rest and painkillers. Veterinary advice must always be sought before taking this approach to avoid hopeless cases being allowed to suffer unnecessarily. As knowledge and skills in the surgical treatment of hamster fracture management improves, the requirement to just leave animals with painful fractures to the powers of nature is thankfully diminishing.

Prognosis: If the bone can be repaired with a pin, these fractures usually heal rapidly, often within three weeks. So long as they cause no problems, the pins need not be removed later. As stated, some fractures heal with nursing care but often with shortened or bent bones. However, so long as there is no chronic pain, this may still be acceptable for a pet animal.

Homeopathic treatment: Homeopathic *Symphytum* and *Calcarea fluorica* will aid and accelerate bone healing. Appropriate fracture support is, of course, still necessary.

Tourniquets/ Constricting Bands ****
Causes: Hamsters are very active little creatures, which greatly adds to their general appeal. However, this also means that we need to be very careful which bedding we choose for them as it is very easy for them to get fibres of bedding twisted around their little legs. These bands then act as tourniquets that constrict the blood vessels that supply oxygen to the leg below this point and lead to gangrene. Certain types of newer synthetic bedding materials seem to be more dangerous in this respect but tourniquets can also result from cotton wool or even with the hamster's own hair in the case of a long haired variety.

Symptoms: The hamster will be lame and may be seen biting at the affected area in an attempt to relieve the stricture. The

160

part of the limb below the band will be cold and may be swollen. Careful examination will show the stricture.

Treatment: It is worth trying to free the obstruction by unravelling the band or gently teasing it apart with tweezers. Be very gentle as the bones are very thin and may have been further weakened by the stricture. If it is impossible to relieve the problem or the animal is in severe pain, then veterinary assistance should be sought immediately. Your vet may need to sedate or anaesthetise the hamster to safely release the band. Anti-inflammatories and antibiotics may be needed afterwards. When the limb has become gangrenous, amputation may need to be considered.

Prognosis: The prognosis should be good so long as the band is removed before permanent damage to the limb occurs. It should become part of your daily health check routine to ensure that nothing has become tangled round your hamster's legs. If you see anything suspicious, it is always worthwhile getting the hamster out of the cage and gently unravelling or loosening the band. Never pull firmly as the bones in the legs are very small and could easily break. Ask your pet shop for advice at the time of purchase of bedding materials as to their safety in this respect.

Homeopathic treatment: If the affected tissues and structures are still viable, homeopathic *Secale* will aid revitalisation. Some surprising recoveries of ischaemic tissues have been witnessed.

Collapsed Hamsters

Heat Stroke ****
Causes: Heat stroke results when the core body temperature remains too high for too long resulting in varying degrees of organ damage. Human mechanisms for eliminating excess

body heat include panting and sweating to encourage heat loss from the body by evaporation of moisture. Hamsters are able to neither sweat nor pant and thus are prone to overheating and heat stroke. Wild golden hamsters are desert dwelling animals that escape heat by burrowing into the sand or moving to cooler areas such as cavities/caves. Unfortunately, the limited space allowed by captivity precludes such natural heat-escape mechanisms. Cages should never be left near a sunny window or in a car in hot weather even for a few minutes.

Symptoms: When exposed to prolonged increases of temperature, the hamsters will get dull and limp before progressing to collapse and shock.

Treatment: The first priority is to remove the hamster from the hot environment. Cooling is best achieved by gently wetting the hamster before using a fan to evaporate this water. Be careful not to overdo the cooling and cause hypothermia instead. The hamsters will need rehydration to avoid the risk of kidney failure later. Your veterinary surgeon may use fluids injected into the abdomen or under the skin. At home, you can use electrolyte rehydration fluids, preferably isotonic, given orally by syringe/tube or dropper.

Prognosis: So long as the problem is detected early and treatment begun while organ damage is still reversible, then the outlook should be good. Avoid the placement of the cage near a glass window, in direct sunlight or near a radiator to prevent heat stroke.

Homeopathic treatment: Homeopathic *Glonoinium* is very helpful in cases of heatstroke, to aid recovery.

Hibernation**

Causes: Hamsters are permissive hibernators. This means that they are capable of putting themselves into a deep sleep or hibernation if adverse environmental conditions occur to conserve energy. The commonest is low environmental temperatures (below 5 degrees Celsius).

Symptoms: The hamster may appear dead because the respiration may be so shallow and slow as to be imperceptible. Equally the pulse and heartbeat will be so slow and weak as to be almost undetectable. The body will be cool to the touch to conserve energy by reducing heat loss.

Treatment: Since it is usually a cold environment that has brought on the hibernation, the reverse should bring the hamster out of this state. The body should be gently warmed on a covered hot-water bottle or in a warm airing cupboard at about 30 degrees Celsius for a few hours. Remember to keep it in its cage or else it may escape on recovery. Once it has recovered, fluids should be administered orally to reduce the risks of later kidney problems secondary to dehydration.

Prognosis: Provided the environmental conditions that lead to the hibernation are rectified, these hamsters should do well later. Domestic central heating systems are often set to turn off during the night while we are asleep to conserve energy and to switch on in the morning before we awake. Since the hamster is nocturnal, however, this means the heating goes off as the hamster awakes with the result that our 'warm' house may still be too cold for the hamster. Electric heat-mats are now available to maintain nocturnal temperatures to avoid this situation. The moral of this section is never to bury a 'dead' hamster until you are certain it is really dead - it may just be hibernating! If in doubt, let your veterinary surgeon have the final say on whether the animal really is dead before proceeding with burial.

Homeopathic treatment: In all cases of collapse or permissive hibernation, homeopathic *Carbo vegetabilis* is of great help. It has been nicknamed the 'homeopathic corpse reviver', on account of its powers in this situation.

Chocolate Toxicity ****

Causes: Human chocolate contains a number of chemicals such as theobromine, which are highly toxic to hamsters.

Symptoms: Soon after access to chocolate or cocoa, the theobromine will initially cause excitement and over-stimulation of the hamster followed by collapse. Diagnosis is mainly by the history of access to the poison combined with the symptoms.

Treatment: Affected hamsters should be taken to a vet immediately as an emergency. They will need intensive nursing with fluids, vitamins and warmth to help detoxify the body.

Prognosis: So long as treatment is begun early in the process, many affected individuals can be saved. Human chocolate should never be fed to hamsters. 'Pet chocolate' is nutritionally safe for animals because it is really just brown fat and contains no real chocolate. However, its sticky consistency may cause cheek pouch impaction and so should be avoided in any case.

Homeopathic treatment: In emergencies, use homeopathic *Nux vomica*. A remedy made from *Chocolate* is available, and can help recovery.

Cage Paralysis ***

Causes: This condition is linked to a lack of exercise, often with an unsuitably small cage with no provision for exercise opportunities such as a wheel.

Symptoms: Affected animals appear stiff and to suffer pain during movement. They may have progressed to total paralysis of the hind legs. X-rays may be required to identify a fractured spine.

Treatment: If the spine has been fractured or there is no pain sensation in the hind legs, then treatment is hopeless and euthanasia should be considered. In less severely affected cases, opportunities for exercise should be introduced. The quality of the diet should be improved with a higher protein content and vitamin supplementation. If pain is shown on movement, then painkillers such as meloxicam may be helpful.

Prognosis: Totally paralysed cases are virtually hopeless while less severely affected cases can show some response with good nursing and treatment.

Homeopathic treatment: Homeopathic *Rhus toxicodendron* and *Conium* are good first aid measures, pending expert veterinary homeopathic help.

Obesity

Obesity **
Causes: Obesity means that an animal is overweight to the point that health is adversely affected. In simple terms, this can only occur if the body is taking in more calories than it is burning up. The excess energy is stored as fat tissue resulting in weight gain.

Symptoms: The hamster will appear overweight and enlarged. It will become lazy due to the effort required for movement, setting up a vicious circle of further weight gain due to decreased energy expenditure via exercise. Gastrointestinal disturbances will lead to chronic soft stools and the accumulation of faeces around the anus. The bones may become osteoporotic due to lack of exercise and predispose to spinal fractures. The expected life span is shortened and the quality of life during life is reduced.

Treatment: It is important to accurately weigh the hamster at the beginning of any dieting process and to set targets for weight loss. Replace starchy and sugary treats that have high energy levels with low-energy high-fibre foods such as vegetables. Avoid the massive over-feeding that is so common among pet hamsters and that allows the hamsters to selectively feed and pick out those rich food items whilst avoiding the lower energy items. Increase exercise progressively as the animal loses weight and gets fitter. Introduce more play outside the cage. Continue weekly weighing and fine-tune the weight loss program as required to give gradual progressive loss until the target weight has been achieved.

Prognosis: With the right approach and attitude, there is no reason why any obese hamster should not be successfully dieted over a period of several weeks. Crash diets are not a good idea as they can lead to severe disease problems due to accumulation of fat in the liver similar to the situation of pregnancy toxaemia.

Homeopathic treatment: Apart from using all the essential management measures, administration of homeopathic *Calcarea carbonica* can aid recovery.

Diabetes Mellitus

Diabetes Mellitus ***
Causes: Diabetes is a disease where there is an increase in the level of blood glucose leading to glucose appearing in the urine. The cause may either be a lack of insulin production or failure of the body to respond to the insulin that is produced. It is relatively common in older hamsters and is an inherited disease in Chinese and Russian hamsters (especially Campbells) as an autosomal recessive trait in some lines and polygenic in others.

Symptoms: The elevated urine glucose levels osmotically draw large volumes of water resulting in a grossly increased urine volume. The hamster will constantly appear thirsty to replace these urine fluid losses. A normal hamster produces 5-8ml urine during a 24-hour period. Weight loss and poor body condition result from the constant loss of glucose from the body as the disease progresses. Cataracts of the eye often develop. The high levels of glucose in the urine predispose the hamster to cystitis. Diagnosis is by finding elevated glucose levels in blood or urine samples on at least two occasions. Due to the difficulty of getting blood samples, urine tests are more commonly used. The test is carried out using a plastic strip with a colour indicator patch at the tip called a DIASTIX. This patch is dipped briefly into fresh urine and, after 30 seconds, the colour is compared against the colour chart provided to record a urine glucose reading. Your vet may gently massage the abdomen to get a urine sample to test in the surgery. Urine can also be collected by housing individual animals in plastic-floored cages with no bedding or carry cases and then waiting for the hamster to pass urine naturally. Colony animals will need to be temporarily isolated to allow testing of each individual. It is possible for a normal non-diabetic hamster to have glucose in the urine. A recent meal such as a honey-based hamster treat can cause glucose to spill over into the urine. For this reason, all such food items should be removed at least 24 hours prior to testing and any positive tests should be repeated before accepting diagnosis.

Treatment: Specific treatment is often not given as many diabetic hamsters live for several months after diagnosis and it is usually older individuals that are affected. Nutritional management can improve the regulation of blood sugar levels without the need for insulin therapy. Hamsters are often provided with a bowl of food that lasts for a day or even two. By reducing the amount of food offered at any one time and increasing the frequency at which food is offered, the animals are encouraged to eat more regularly. Avoid treats that contain sugars, honey or molasses. Switch to healthier treats such as vegetables or the leaves of safe wild plants. Avoid feeding foods such as nuts that are high in fats. Dietary fibre helps to stabilise blood glucose levels so the addition of fibre sources such as bran or hay will help. Vitamin and essential fatty acid supplementation help to improve metabolism (see Chapter 4 for further discussion on dietary options). The large volumes of urine passed will require regular changes of cage bedding to avoid unpleasant odours and skin problems from urine scalding and reduce the risks from aspergillosis.

Treatment may be attempted using insulin as for other pets. The average daily dose required is 2iu insulin given by subcutaneous injection but initial stabilisation should begin at a fraction of this level. There are no orally active versions of insulin available to avoid the requirement for daily injections. During initial stabilisation, urine should be tested daily. The optimum time for testing is about 8 hours following insulin administration. The insulin dose should be varied until urine glucose is just about detectable. Daily testing and treatment should continue for life.

It is important to be aware that insulin treatment can result in the blood sugar levels dropping too low. This is called hypoglycaemia. The hamster will become inco-ordinated at first before progressing to total collapse. In such situations, a ready source of glucose should be given immediately and your veterinary surgeon contacted. Honey can be rubbed into the gums or a glucose solution dropped into the mouth or by injection.

Prognosis: Many hamsters live several happy months after diagnosis. Since hamster vision is poor anyway, the presence of cataracts is not that important. Affected individuals and their close relatives should not be used for breeding to avoid passing on these diabetic genes.

Homeopathic treatment: Diabetes mellitus can often respond to homeopathic input, but this requires expert homeopathic veterinary guidance, on account of the complexity and seriousness of the disease.

Chapter 8

Pharmacy

Introduction

Throughout this book, numerous drugs have been mentioned. This chapter details the indications for and dosages of some of these medications. It is worth stressing that many of these drugs are legally classed as 'prescription only medications' (POM). This means that they can only be dispensed and used under the authorisation of a veterinary surgeon and for the specific animal intended.

It is also worth stressing that very few medicines have a product license allowing use in hamsters. However, in the absence of licensed drugs for use in hamsters, it is allowable to use a drug licensed for the same condition in another species. This does mean that there is often no specified dose by the manufacturer for hamsters. Accepted dose rates have often been developed based on the personal experience of the attending veterinary surgeon and information taken from literature based on other veterinary surgeons' experiences.

Safe use of all medications implies that the hamster be weighed accurately on reliable scales and not just have a guessed weight. It is important to remember that drug therapy is only one part of treating your hamster. Successful therapy also includes nursing, nutrition and that ever-so-important factor of tender loving care (TLC) that is so easy to overlook.

Some homeopathic medicines are also listed. These have lesser legal restrictions for home use and body weight is not important but you are still advised to seek expert homeopathic veterinary help to gain maximum benefit from this form of therapy.

Safe reliable administration of medication is as important as the choice of drug therapy itself. Very few medications have been manufactured with hamsters as the intended patient. Thus it is often necessary to split down larger medications intended for dogs and cats to the concentration and doses that hamsters require. At the veterinary surgery, your vet can be certain that the medicine is properly administered by injecting the hamster but administration may be more complicated at home.

The old adage about taking a horse to water but not being able to make it drink could refer just as well to medications added to the drinking water of hamsters. Liquid preparations, such as the antibiotic enrofloxacin, are easily added to the drinking water but this does not automatically mean that the patient will drink. The animal may be too sick to drink or the medication may impart an unpleasant taste to the water. Furthermore, in colony situations, the more dominant individuals may prevent access by the sick hamster to the water. Addition of sugar or flavoured children's cordial drinks to the water may help overcome the taste problem but the only certain way of administering the correct dose is to put the liquid medication directly into the animal's mouth via a syringe or dropper. Tablets can be crushed down and powdered onto dampened food so the particles stick to the food. Allowance needs to be made for the proportion of such medication that is not ingested when calculating the dose. The powder may also be mixed with something sweet and sticky such as honey or jam that can then be smeared in or near the mouth to encourage swallowing. Some medications, such as the mange treatment ivermectin, work very well by application directly to the skin when mixed with propylene glycol from where they are absorbed through the skin into the body. Ask your veterinary surgeon for advice on the best method of administration for individual drugs.

Remember that prescribed medications are intended for use on the hamster only and should not be allowed to come into direct contact with the human body. Some may be directly toxic to humans such as griseofulvin while others may present allergic hazards to humans such as certain antibiotics. Gloves should always be worn when handling and administering medications. Masks should be worn whenever grinding medications or dealing with powdered drugs. Any accidental contact of medications to skin or mucous membranes should be washed off immediately with water and medical advice sought.

Many medications are available from several different manufacturers with presentations of different formulations and concentrations. An example of one brand and manufacturer is shown for most drugs listed here. This does not imply that this is the best or the only brand, merely that it is the brand the author has had most experience with.

The overall message is that there is more to medicating your sick hamster than just picking a drug from a list. You should be guided by your veterinary surgeon. Remember that the field of hamster medicine is an exciting and rapidly growing one as more work by veterinary surgeons, pharmaceutical companies, teaching institutions and most importantly committed owners leads to increased knowledge.

Some of the important medicines along with their uses and doses are given overleaf.

Conventional Medicine

Pharmacy

Ace-High (Vetark Professional): Ace-High is a special vitamin and mineral supplement, formulated to provide high levels of the vitamins A, C and E along with smaller quantities of other vitamins and minerals. Rodents such as hamsters have relatively poor immune systems and vitamins such as A and E are involved in helping the body to resist infection. Vitamin A is essential for the maintenance of healthy mucous membranes such as in the mouth, lungs and gut. Vitamin E has been shown to boost the immune system and Vitamin C is used up very quickly when the body is under stress and must be replaced.

Aspirin: Acetylsalicylic acid, commonly known as aspirin, can be used as a painkiller in emergency situations. The dose is 100-150mg/kg given orally every 4 hours. Standard tablets contain 300mg aspirin although 75mg tablets are also available. A crude hamster dose would be 1/25th of a 300mg tablet.

Amitraz **POM**: Amitraz (ALUDEX Intervet UK Ltd) is an effective treatment for all kinds of mange mites. It should be applied to cover the entire skin area using soaked cotton balls to avoid the risk of toxicity from accidental ingestion during direct dipping. It should not be rinsed off to permit prolonged activity. The standard preparation available contains 50g/litre and the effective concentration is achieved by adding 1.4ml of the concentrate to 1 litre of warm water. It is important to keep the animals warm after use to reduce any sedation caused by the treatment. Some animals may initially appear itchier as the mites die in their skin. Low levels of short-term anti-inflammatories may be required to reduce this itching. The treatment will need to be repeated every 14 days for 3-6 treatments or for as long as mites remain visible on skin scrapes. There are some reports that

174

Amitraz may be toxic to some hamsters despite these precautions so an alternative treatment may be advisable where available.

Ark-Klens (Vetark Professional): This is a blend of benzalkonium chloride specially selected for safety of use. These are powerful disinfectants with an additional detergent and very good deodorising action. At the recommended concentration, it is non-corrosive, bactericidal against a wide range of gram-negative and gram-positive bacteria as well as being effective against some viruses and fungi. This makes ARK-KLENS suitable for disinfection of the animal environment such as cages and food and water bowls and bottles. General disinfection is carried out using 10ml/5 litres water.

Arkvits (Vetark Professional): Arkvits is ideal for the routine supplementation of hamsters with vitamins and minerals. It is especially useful for breeding animals which are perpetually in need of calcium and require 'topping up' on their vitamin levels.

Avipro (Vetark Professional): Avipro is a probiotic combination of bacteria, enzymes, electrolytes and vitamins. Its high palatability means it can be added to the drinking water making its use simple. For general use as a routine nutritional aid, 1 scoop per 200ml drinking water can be used. This is especially useful when animals are newly purchased or are under stress due to illness, breeding or in very warm, humid weather. Avipro is particularly useful for hamsters undergoing antibiotic treatment when the normal gut flora may be seriously unbalanced by the treatment leading to the establishment of inappropriate bacteria, many of which can form toxins. It helps to minimise any disturbance to the normal gut flora caused by the use of antibiotics. For support of very stressed animals or for use to reduce the risks of digestive disturbances with the use of oral antibiotics, use 1 scoop (4g) per 100ml drinking water.

CANAURAL EAR DROPS POM Leo Laboratories Ltd: Canaural eardrops are effective against the microorganisms commonly associated with ear infections including ear mites. They contain fusidic acid (antibiotic), framycetin (antibiotic), nystatin (anti-fungal) and prednisolone (corticosteroid). One drop can be applied to each ear twice daily. Hamster ears need to be handled very gently when treating as the fragile blood vessels supplying the ears are easily damaged leading to gangrene. Canaural eardrops have an oily formulation that helps to soften the waxy material in the ear but will result in the facial area becoming very greasy during treatment.

Carprofen **POM**: (RIMADYL SMALL ANIMAL INJECTION Pfizer Ltd) Carprofen is a non-steroidal anti-inflammatory drug with pain-relieving and fever-reducing properties. It is used for pain from musculo-skeletal disorders and post-surgery. Rimadyl Small Animal Injection contains 50mg of carprofen per ml and the dose is 4mg/kg as a one-off injection. This equates to a dose of 0.01ml per 125g hamster. The injectable version cannot be administered orally. Tablets are also available.

Chloramphenicol **POM**: (CHLOROMYCETIN V REDIDROPS Pharmacia & Upjohn) Chloramphenicol is a broad spectrum antibiotic with activity against most types of bacteria and some chlamydia. It is useful in the case of conjunctivitis or other eye infections of bacterial or chlamydial origin. The use of chloramphenicol should be restricted to those cases where clinical experience and preferably laboratory testing has shown it to be the best choice. This results from the important role of this antibiotic in the treatment of Salmonella infections in humans and the need to keep usage low to reduce bacterial resistance. Chloromycetin V Redidrops appear to be well tolerated in the eye and to penetrate well into the eye following ophthalmic administration. One drop should be applied to the eye every 3 hours and treatment should be continued for at least 48 hours after the eye appears normal. Chloramphenicol succinate can also be given by injection at a dose of 30mg/kg every 12 hours or chloramphenicol palmitate given orally at a dose of 50mg/kg every 8 hours.

Chlorhexidine: (HIBISCRUB) Chlorhexidine is an antiseptic with antifungal action suitable for skin application. Contact time of at least 1 minute is very important to allow bacteria and fungi to be inactivated. It can be diluted 1:100 with warm water to flush contaminated wounds.

Corticosteroids POM: (BETSOLAN SOLUBLE Fort Dodge Animal Health Ltd) (DEXADRESON Intervet UK Ltd) There are many different types of corticosteroids available with slightly different characteristics. Betsolan Soluble is a clear aqueous solution of 2mg bethamethasone phosphate per ml. Corticosteroids are anti-inflammatories and are useful in the treatment of shock and circulatory collapse. The dose varies with the condition but 0.01- 0.02ml per 100g hamster should be effective. Dexadreson contains 2mg per ml of dexamethasone sodium phosphate. The anti-shock dose for a hamster is 4-5mg/kg given intra-muscularly. This equates to 0.2ml of Dexadreson per 100g hamster. Treatment should only need to be administered once. Pregnant animals should not be treated as it can lead to abortion. Corticosteroids may delay wound healing and are immunosuppressant and thus antibiotic cover may need to be used during treatment.

DERMISOL MULTICLEANSE SOLUTION Pfizer Ltd is a clear liquid containing a mixture of mild acids and propylene glycol. It aids the healing of wounds by cleansing and removing dead tissue from the affected area. It can be applied 2-3 times daily for as long as required.

Doxycycline **POM**: (RONAXAN 20mg Merial Animal Health Ltd) Doxycycline is a tetracycline antibiotic particularly effective against respiratory infections. The dose is 2.5mg/kg daily. Unfortunately, the smallest veterinary-licensed tablets are 20mg so a 100g hamster would require 1% of a 20mg tablet. This could be crushed and added to any particularly soft food such as honey that the hamster would readily eat.

Electrolyte Solutions: (LIQUID LECTADE Pfizer Ltd) Electrolyte solutions are useful oral rehydration therapy for reversing the process of dehydration and loss of electrolytes following diarrhoea. They are also used as an aid in post-operative care where rehydration is required in the recovery period. Liquid Lectade is an example of these electrolyte solutions. The addition of 8ml Liquid Lectade with 92ml water gives 100ml of isotonic solution. This can be offered in place of the drinking water and the addition of a small amount of concentrated fruit juice may make it more palatable. Alternatively, administration can be orally at a rate of up to 25ml/kg per day split into several small doses and continued for 3-6 days or as required. The solution needs to be made up fresh daily.

Enilconazole: (IMAVEROL Janssen Animal Health) Enilconazole is an antifungal that can be used as a wash or a dip to treat ringworm. The standard concentrated preparation available contains 100mg/ml and needs to be diluted by adding one part concentrate to 50 parts of lukewarm water. The entire body needs to be wetted at each application taking care to avoid getting it onto the eyes and treatment will need to be repeated at 3-day intervals at least 4 times. Longhaired hamsters should be clipped before treatment and have any large crusts removed.

Enrofloxacin **POM**: (BAYTRIL Bayer plc) Enrofloxacin is one of the best and safest antibiotics for hamsters. It has been widely used for many years and has a broad spectrum of activity. It is well absorbed from the intestine and will travel to most parts of the body. The dose is 5mg/kg given twice daily or 10mg/kg once daily for at least 7 days. It is available as a 2.5% injection or 2.5% oral solution. Your vet may begin the course with an injection of about 0.04ml to a 100g hamster. Medication at home can be via the drinking water at a dose of 0.2ml per 100mls water. This solution needs to be made up fresh each day, as it is unstable in light. Because daily water intake may vary between hamsters and especially if they are sick, it is better to administer the drug directly orally. As a rough guide, a dilution of 1:4 with sweet fruit juice usually means a twice-daily dose of 2 drops twice daily of the mixture to dwarf hamsters and 4 drops twice daily to Syrian hamsters. Alternatively, the required amount can be dropped onto a favourite food and fed in this way.

Erythromycin **POM**: (ERYTHROCIN SOLUBLE Ceva Animal Health Ltd) Erythromycin is an antibiotic that is useful as an aid in the prevention of 'Wet Tail' in colonies. It is available as a powder where each 70g sachet contains 11.56g of erythromycin. Addition of one sachet to 115 litres of water gives a working dilution of 100mg/litre. The solution should be made up fresh every 24 hours. Care needs to be taken with erythromycin, as it is one of those antibiotics that potentially can lead to overgrowth of bowel bacteria.

Fenbendazole **POM**: (PANACUR 2.5% LIQUID Hoechst Roussel Vet Ltd) Fenbendazole is a broad-spectrum wormer for the treatment of gastro-intestinal roundworms and tapeworms. The dose is 20mg/kg given orally once daily for 5 days. The 2.5% preparation contains 25mg/ml equating to a dose of 0.1ml daily for 5 days to a 125g hamster. This dose can be doubled to 50mg/ml and used for 5 consecutive days to treat Giardia, a protozoal bowel parasite that can be passed to humans.

Fipronil **POM**: (FRONTLINE SPRAY Merial Animal Health Ltd) Fipronil is an insecticidal spray effective against fleas, ticks and some types of mites. The dose is 3ml/kg that equates to 6 pumps per kg of the 100ml presentation. The required amount should be sprayed onto a gloved hand and then applied all over the body of the hamster but avoiding contact with the eyes. It should be allowed to dry naturally and not towel dried. Since the spray is in an alcohol base, good ventilation and a warm environment are important after treatment. Treatment is repeated every 30-60 days.

Frusemide **POM**: (LASIX 5% SOLUTION Hoechst Roussel Vet Ltd) Frusemide is a rapid onset diuretic that results in increased urine production and thus helps the body to eliminate fluids that may have accumulated in the lungs, lower limbs or abdomen due to heart, liver or kidney failure. The dose is 5-10mg/kg given by injection every 12 hours. Lasix 5% contains 50mg/ml frusemide giving a dose of 0.1-0.2 ml per hamster.

FUSIDIC ACID **POM**: Fusidic acid is an antibiotic that is active against Staphylococci, one of the main types of organisms associated with skin infections. It is available as a cream licensed for human use called FUCIDIN Leo Laboratories Ltd or in combination with a corticosteroid (bethamethasone) in a veterinary licensed gel called FUCIDERM Leo Laboratories Ltd. In both cases, a small amount of the preparation should be applied twice daily to affected areas of skin for 5 days.

FUCITHALMIC VET (Leo Laboratories Ltd) **POM**: Fucithalmic Vet is a sterile viscous eye drop of 1% aqueous sustained release formulation of fusidic acid useful in cases of bacterial conjunctivitis. The fusidic acid is an antibiotic active against Staphylococci bacteria and the sustained release formulation ensures that once or twice daily application gives 24 hours of activity. The viscous gel base also reduces corneal irritation by increasing lubrication during eyelid blinking.

Griseofulvin **POM**: (GRISOVIN Fort Dodge Animal Health Ltd) Griseofulvin is an antifungal used in the treatment of ringworm. The dose is 25-50 mg/kg given twice daily orally. Administration must be continued until a new outer layer of skin has grown and all the old outer skin has shed. This will be for at least 4 weeks or until a veterinary surgeon confirms that the animal has been cured. Tablets contain 125mg griseofulvin. As a guide to dosing, assume that only 10% of any dry medication added to the food will be ingested. This means that a quarter of a tablet can be crushed and added to the dry food mix twice daily. Always wear gloves when handling griseofulvin as it has been shown to affect the unborn foetus and never administer to pregnant animals. Hair around the affected area should be clipped every 14 days during treatment. Remember that fungal spores can remain on the coat and in the environment even after treatment and that this disease can spread to humans (zoonosis).

Ibuprofen: Ibuprofen is a non-steroidal anti-inflammatory that is widely used for human treatment. It can be given at a dose of 280mg/kg orally pre-surgery or 70mg/kg orally after surgery for pain relief. In dogs and cats, it has been associated with kidney and stomach ulcer side effects and may cause the same in hamsters.

Insulin **POM**: (INSUVET PROTAMINE ZINC Fort Dodge Animal Health Ltd) Insulin is a hormone produced by the pancreas and helps the body to lower blood glucose. Diabetes mellitus results from a partial or complete lack of insulin production. Treatment for diabetes is via daily injections of insulin. Insuvet contains 100iu insulin per 1ml. An average daily dose per hamster of 2iu insulin equates to 0.02ml Insuvet daily. Insuvet may be diluted with sterile water to make dosing more accurate. The resultant dilution is stable for 28 days but should be refrigerated.

Ivermectin **POM**: (PANOMEC Injection for cattle, sheep and pigs Merial Animal Health Ltd) Ivermectin is an extremely effective treatment for virtually all parasites that live either in or on hamsters (the exception being that it does not kill tapeworms). Its main use in hamsters is for the treatment of mange but it is also effective against intestinal pinworms. The standard preparation contains 10mg/ml ivermectin and the dose is 0.2 - 0.5mg/kg. Application can be by injection, oral administration or topical skin application of a dilution with propylene glycol. For topical use, a 1:9 dilution with propylene glycol is often used resulting in a dose of 0.1- 0.2 ml of the dilution per 500g bodyweight. Ivermectin does not kill the mite eggs so treatment should be repeated every 7-10 days for 2-4 treatments to kill newly-hatched immature mites before they get an opportunity to breed and thus to break the life cycle.

Kaolin and Pectin Suspension: (KAOGEL V Pharmacia & Upjohn Ltd) Kaogel V is a smooth free-flowing orange-yellow suspension with a fruit-like odour containing light kaolin and pectin. It is administered orally at a dose of 1-2ml/kg equating to 2-3 drops per 100g hamster given 3 times daily. It is useful as an aid in the treatment of non-specific diarrhoeas.

Marbofloxacin **POM**: (MARBOCYL SA Vetoquinol UK Ltd) Marbofloxacin is a broad-spectrum bactericidal antibiotic that is beginning to be accepted for use in small animals such as hamsters. The therapeutic dose is 2-5 mg/kg/day. The standard injectable version contains 10mg/ml so a 100g hamster would require 0.2-0.5 ml per day. This can be administered either by injection or orally. Since 1ml equates to 40 drops, this would mean oral administration of 1-2 drops daily. Should direct administration be impossible, it can be used at a dose of 0.2-0.4 ml (8-16 drops) per 100ml drinking water but variations in water intake between individuals makes this method less accurate. Addition of sweet fruit juice to the water, such as blackcurrant, may encourage drinking. Medicated water should be protected from bright sunlight and replaced daily.

MAXITROL EYE DROPS **POM** (Alcon-Couvreur NV): contain a steroid, dexamethasone, which is an anti-inflammatory agent and is present to reduce ocular irritation. Maxitrol also contains two antibiotics, polymixin B sulphate and neomycin sulphate, which act against bacterial organisms that cause infection. One drop is applied to the eye surface up to 6 times daily for up to 5 days. Medicines should not be used more than one month after opening.

Meloxicam **POM**: (METACAM ORAL SUSPENSION Boehringer Ingelheim Ltd) Meloxicam is a potent non-steroidal anti-inflammatory agent. It is used for the alleviation of pain and inflammation associated with the musculo-skeletal system. It is available as an injection containing 5mg/ml meloxicam or as an oral suspension containing 1.5mg/ml. Initial dosing is at 0.2mg/kg and can be continued long-term as required or slowly reduced to the lowest effective dose. Should the initial dose not be effective, 0.4mg/kg could be used short-term. The oral suspension has the odour and taste of honey that many hamsters find very appealing. One drop of the oral suspension contains 0.05mg meloxicam so half a drop would treat a 125g-hamster daily at the 0.2mg/kg dose.

Metronidazole **POM**: (TORGYL SOLUTION Merial Animal Health Ltd) Metronidazole is an antibiotic that is effective against anaerobic bacteria and is useful in treating digestive upsets and 'wet tail'. Dose is 20 - 60 mg/kg given twice daily. The standard liquid preparation contains 5mg/ml, allowing dosing for an average Syrian hamster of 0.5ml twice daily. Alternatively, 20ml can be added to 1 litre of drinking water with added sugar to increase palatability. It can also be used to flush and clean abscesses and other wounds.

Natamycin **POM**: (MYCOPHYT Intervet UK Ltd) Natamycin is an antifungal that can be used as a wash to treat animals affected with ringworm. The standard preparation contains 1g natamycin per 10g. 1g of this concentrate is mixed with 1 litre of warm water and used as a dip for affected animals. It is important to allow the liquid to dry into the coat and not to rinse it off. Care should be taken to avoid contact of the wash with the animal's eyes. Treatment should be repeated after 4 - 5 days and again after 14 days.

NEOBIOTIC HC DROPS and NEOBIOTIC EYE OINTMENT **POM** (Pharmacia & Upjohn Ltd). Both products contain neomycin, an antibiotic that is effective against many bacterial causes of eye infections. Neobiotic HC drops also contain hydrocortisone that is an effective anti-inflammatory. Treatment needs to be applied 3 - 6 times daily for up to 7 days.

Neomycin **POM**: (NEOBIOTIC PUMP Pharmacia & Upjohn Ltd) Neomycin is an oral antibiotic that is not well absorbed from the intestine and is useful in the treatment of diarrhoea. The standard preparation available contains 50mg/ml and the dose is 100 mg/kg daily for 5-7 days allowing a dose of 0.2ml daily orally to a Syrian hamster. Alternatively, it can be added to the drinking water at 10ml per litre to make a dilution of 0.5mg/ml water.

Oxytetracycline **POM**: (TERRAMYCIN SOLUBLE POWDER Pfizer Ltd) Oxytetracycline is an antibiotic that has been around for many years and has a broad spectrum of activity. The oral dose is 55 mg/kg per day split into 3 doses and administered in either the food or drinking water. The standard preparation contains 55g/kg in a water-soluble base and comes with a spoon that holds 240mg oxytetracycline. Addition of one level spoon to one litre of water gives a working dilution of 240mg/litre that tends to be correct for use as a drinking water medication. The solution needs to be made up fresh every 24 hours. Injectable oxytetracycline may also be administered by injection at a dose of 10mg/kg every 12 hours or 16mg/kg given once daily.

Paracetamol: Paracetamol (also called acetaminophen) (CALPOL PAEDIATRIC Warner Lambert) can be used as a painkiller in emergency situations. The dose is 1-2mg/ml of drinking water. The commercially available paediatric suspensions contain 120mg/5ml so addition of 5ml per 100ml drinking water gives an acceptable level of 1.2 mg/ml with the added bonus that the strawberry flavour should encourage drinking.

Piperazine citrate: Piperazine is used to treat intestinal pinworm infestations. Standard liquid preparations (ANTEPAR ELIXIR Welcome) contain 150mg/ml Piperazine. The dose is 20mg daily for an adult hamster with treatment given for 7 days, stopped for 7 days and then repeated for 7 days. This means a daily dose of 0.13ml per adult hamster. Alternatively, oral dosing can be effected by adding 2-5 ml of the concentrate to 150mls of water to achieve 2-5mg/ml of drinking water.

Povidone-Iodine: (PEVIDINE) Povidone-iodine is a useful antiseptic for the treatment of both bacterial and fungal skin infections. It tends to stain contact areas a dark brown colour, which can be useful to show up those areas that have been treated. It can be diluted 1:5 and used as a wash. As for all antiseptics, increasing the contact time by delaying or avoiding rinsing increases efficacy.

Praziquantal: (DRONCIT TABLETS Bayer plc) Praziquantal is a highly effective treatment for most adult forms of tapeworm. The dose is 6-10mg/kg given orally. Standard tablets contain 50mg praziquantal requiring only 1/50th of a tablet per hamster.

S.A.Vits (Vetark Professional): S.A.Vits is an easy-to-use formulation of water-soluble vitamins high in vitamins A and C. They are palatable and ideal for hamsters as a routine every-day supplement.

Tamodine (Vetark Professional): This is a tamed iodine preparation for dressing wounds and bites. It may be more appropriate than creams and ointments for animals like hamsters that groom. Any excess should be wiped off after application.

Tamodine E (Vetark Professional): Tamodine E is an iodophore disinfectant suitable for general-purpose cage disinfection. It is a brownish viscous liquid, the colour acting as a useful marker to show areas have been cleaned. It is effective against a slightly wider range of bacteria, viruses and fungi than Ark-Klens. A standard wash solution is obtained by adding 4.5ml per litre water but this can be doubled to 9ml per litre for heavily soiled or porous surfaces. For critical situations where the ultimate in disinfection is required, then a two-phase cleaning with Ark-Klens followed by disinfection with Tamodine-E gives extra security.

Tiacil Ophthalmic Solution (Virbac Ltd) **POM**: Tiacil ophthalmic solution is a sterile eye drop containing gentamicin, a bactericidal antibiotic active against most gram-positive and gram-negative bacteria responsible for ocular infections. After administration, Tiacil covers the cornea with effective levels of antibiotic for no less than 6 hours. One drop should be applied to the eye three times daily for 7 days.

Trimethoprim / Sulphonamide **POM**: (BORGAL 7.5% SOLUTION Intervet UK Ltd) There are a number of different sulphonamides that are combined with trimethoprim to act as a very effective broad-spectrum anti-bacterial agent. Each ml of BORGAL contains 62.5mg sulfadoxine and 12.5mg trimethoprim. The daily dose of 30mg/kg of the combination can be achieved by administering 0.2ml that can be given by injection or orally.

VISCOTEARS Novartis Ophthalmics. This is a carbomer liquid gel that is preservative free. A single drop can be applied to the eye four times daily to reduce irritation during blinking in cases of eyelid deformity, deficiency of tear production or microphthalmia.

Dangerous Medications
Of almost equal importance to understanding the role of useful medications for treatment of sick hamsters is the need to avoid those medications that may be dangerous. Being safe in one species does not mean that a drug will be safe in all other species. There are many differences between the species in how the body deals with chemicals administered to them. This is why some drugs such as thalidomide used in humans have had disastrous side effects despite coming through animal testing in several species without showing problems.

Hamster medicine is still in its infancy but due to the current popularity of these charming little animals, it is on a steep learning curve. Some of those medications with the potential for toxic effects in hamsters are given below but this list is likely to increase.

Antibiotics with Side Effects for Hamsters
Bacitracin **POM**: Enteritis and antibiotic associated clostridial entero-toxaemia. Incidence is higher when given orally.

Cephalosporins **POM**: Enteritis and antibiotic associated clostridial entero-toxaemia. Incidence is higher when given orally.

Clindamycin **POM**: Enteritis and antibiotic associated clostridial entero-toxaemia. Incidence is higher when given orally.

Erythromycin **POM**: Enteritis and antibiotic associated clostridial entero-toxaemia. Incidence is higher when given orally. Despite this, erythromycin may still be useful in the prevention of 'wet tail'.

Gentamicin **POM**: Enteritis and antibiotic associated clostridial entero-toxaemia. Incidence is higher when given orally.

Lincomycin **POM**: Enteritis and antibiotic associated clostridial entero-toxaemia. Incidence is higher when given orally.

Penicillins including *ampicillin* and *amoxycillin* **POM**: Enteritis and antibiotic associated clostridial entero-toxaemia. Incidence is higher when given orally.

Streptomycin and *dihydrostreptomycin* **POM**: Enteritis and antibiotic associated clostridial entero-toxaemia. Incidence is higher when given orally. These antibiotics can also cause ascending flaccid paralysis and death.

Tylosin **POM**: Enteritis and antibiotic associated clostridial entero-toxaemia. Incidence is higher when given orally.

Vancomycin **POM**: Enteritis and antibiotic associated clostridial entero-toxaemia. Incidence is higher when given orally.

Homeopathic Medicines

Care and administration of homeopathic medicines
Homeopathic medicines are very delicate, therefore you
should avoid touching the medicine with your hand. Do not
return accidentally handled medicine to the bottle and
dispense just the required dose from the bottle at each dosage
time. Keep the container tightly sealed at all times, except
when dispensing. Do not open two containers of medicine at
once. Medicines should be stored away from sunlight, in a
cool dark place and kept away from strong-smelling
substances, especially camphor, embrocations, perfume etc.
They should not be refrigerated or frozen. If correctly stored,
homeopathic medicines can survive for very long periods, so
do not discard unused supplies; they could be useful to your
animal (or for yourself) in the future.

Pillules may conveniently be dispensed into the bottle cap
prior to dosing. It is not necessary to give an exact number of
pillules. In the case of treating hamsters the pillules may be
dissolved in a little boiled, cooled water and administered
from a syringe (without the needle) as a means of liquid
dosing. Alternatively, a different form of the medicine could
be supplied (e.g. tablets which can be crushed in paper or
drops supplied in a dropper bottle). Solid preparations may
also be dissolved in the drinking water, replaced freshly each
day, for convenience and stress avoidance.

Drops may be given in water or directly into the mouth. One
to three drops is a usual dose.

Injections are available from a homeopathic vet.

Lotions are for external use only. These should usually be
diluted prior to use.

If giving homeopathic medicines by mouth, ensure that the dose is either swallowed or retained in the mouth for 30 seconds; thereafter it may be ejected without diminishing the effect. When more than one medicine has been prescribed please do not give at the same time. If possible, allow a five-minute interval between different prescriptions. If possible, do not give within 15 minutes of food. In the case of hamsters pillules may be added to the drinking water, freshly prepared each day.

Useful Homeopathic Remedies

Aconite: Any condition involving or arising from shock, fright or panic. Also treats sudden onset fevers, cold or heat exposure, and acute stress.

Æsculus: A medicine that can treat venous engorgement and stasis. May be useful in cases of rectal prolapse.

Arnica: This remedy will help to treat any injury, minimising bruising and tissue damage. Other first-aid remedies may be required in addition, according to the specific nature of the injury or surgery.

Arsenicum: This medicine fits the animal that is fastidious, warmth loving and suffering corrosive discharges. It is also one of homeopathy's many diarrhoea remedies, when symptoms/signs are appropriate.

Calc. Fluor: A remedy that aids calcium absorption and metabolism, with particular benefits in bone and tooth development.

Calc. Phos: This medicine aids calcium metabolism and absorption, helping the strength of skeleton and teeth. It particularly suits an animal that tends to run lean.

Calendula Lotion: Use in diluted form (one drop in ten) for bathing open wounds of any description. It is antiseptic and stimulates healing.

Carbo veg: A medicine with particular effects in the digestive system, treating gaseous accumulation. It has a reputation as the homeopathic 'corpse reviver', since it greatly helps in any state of collapse. Animals with respiratory problems needing its help usually display an obvious air hunger. May help in emergencies, to revive a collapsed hamster, especially one that may have become seriously chilled.

Carcinosin: A powerful nosode. Use only under expert homeopathic veterinary guidance.

Euphrasia: Helps any eye complaint. It particularly fits cases that have been exacerbated by cold draughts of air.

Graphites: This remedy has its best action in fatter, lazy animals, with a tendency to a smelly skin. Skin lesions can show crusts and serous, sticky discharges.

Hepar sulph: This will help acute suppurative conditions. Typical lesions are usually extremely painful to touch.

Hypericum: This homeopathic remedy can be thought of a little like a painkiller, especially useful in cases of injury to extremities or areas rich in nerve endings. Use when there has been an injury to a toe or ear. In small animals with tails, this also treats painful tail injuries very well.

Ledum: Use this remedy when there has been a puncture wound. It is very useful, for instance, in the unlikely case of cat bite injury.

Merc. corr. - No other remedy has a better record in the treatment of acute eye ulcers. It may also treat diarrhoea, where there is great drama and straining. Suitable patients usually display a great thirst with a paradoxically wet mouth.

Merc. sol: This is very similar to Merc. corr., but symptoms are usually less dramatic. It will usually help more chronic eye ulcers.

Natrum carb: This is a medicine suited to those animals that have a great sensitivity to dietary disturbance and changes. Diarrhoea is a chief symptom.

Natrum sulph: This is a useful remedy to help, in addition to Arnica, in cases of head injury.

Nux vomica: - Any animal who has been overfed on rich food or pellets, or who may have gained accidental access to a store of food, should be given Nux in an attempt to prevent the trouble that can ensue. It will also help even when symptoms emerge.

Psorinum: Primarily a medicine for use with a greasy skin in a hamster that avidly seeks warmth and covering.

Pulsatilla: This remedy has a picture of muco-purulent discharges, which may be greenish-yellow and which are usually worse in the evening. A typical patient is not at all thirsty.

Ruta graveolens: Useful in any joint or ligament sprain.

Sabadilla: Sneezing with eye or nose discharges are characteristic of patients requiring Sabadilla.

Secale: This remedy will help salvage compromised circulation in injured dependent parts (e.g. paws, tails, ear lobes etc.).

Silica: Any chronic or incomplete suppurative process will usually be accelerated and resolved by giving Silica. It may also help ejection by tissues of penetrating foreign bodies. Fibreglass wool padding (e.g. for roof insulation) may become embedded painfully in skin and require the help of Silica for rejection and healing.

Spongia: This helps respiratory problems, especially those caused by heart inadequacy.

Sulphur: Primarily a remedy for use in skin affections, especially when the patient tends to avoid warmth and the skin looks dirty.

Symphytum: Helps with any injury to bone, speeding healing and lessening pain. It also has a reputation in helping injuries to the eyeball itself.

Tub. Bov: A powerful nosode. Use only under expert homeopathic veterinary guidance.

See Appendix II for homeopathic remedies that are recommended for inclusion in your first aid box.

Other Alternative (Non-Homeopathic) Remedies

Aloe Vera: can be given in different ways, either in your hamster's water or directly on their skin. If treating a skin condition apply either Aloe Vera spray or gel at least once a day until the symptoms clear. Ensure that the spray or gel is safe for internal use, just in case your hamster decides to lick it off. Aloe Vera drinks are available; some have been flavoured with fruit juice, which will make it more palatable for your hamster. Due to the large size bottles of Aloe Vera juice drink, you will probably need to drink it too! Some Aloe Vera products have been developed especially for animals.

Echinacea (herbal tincture): is renowned for helping boost the immune system. It should not be given in the long term. Put one drop in the drinking water daily. Use this if your hamster either has or is about to undergo surgery in order to boost their immune system.

Bach Flower Remedies: These remedies work on different emotional states. They are extremely subtle in their application and can have tremendously beneficial effects on both humans and animals. There are many books on flower remedies, which outline the different emotional states that they treat. Leaflets are also available giving a quick reference guide to the remedy needed. However, Rescue™ Remedy is ideal for treating pets that have suffered a trauma or accident. For those who are pining the loss of a partner or member of the litter, Star of Bethlehem treats grief. Walnut can be used if one has to be separated from others in a colony to help it settle and adjust to the change. Mix two or three drops in a glass of water and put in their water bottle. In emergency, using a dropper, put one or two drops of the diluted remedy directly in their mouth.

Chapter 9

Euthanasia

A positive approach

Euthanasia means deliberately bringing about the death of an animal. It is also sometimes called 'putting to sleep' or 'putting down'. It may be the hardest decision ever made by a pet owner. It needs to be properly thought through by the owner and compassionately performed by the veterinary surgeon to avoid emotional problems later. Due to the short natural life span of hamsters compared with most other animals, the need to make this decision may sadly arise relatively soon after first getting your hamster. This can be especially traumatic for children. Even for the experienced hamster keeper, euthanasia is a subject that doesn't get any easier with time and exposure.

Euthanasia needs to be approached from a positive point of view. In many ways it is the greatest gift that can be given to an animal that is suffering. Your pet can be painlessly put to sleep and will never suffer again. Your veterinary surgeon will help you decide whether it is necessary to have your pet put to sleep and when the time is right. You will normally be asked to sign a consent form at the time of euthanasia.

Reasons for Euthanasia

The most important factor when considering euthanasia is whether your pet is suffering and whether this suffering can be effectively relieved. The nature and prognosis of the illness and the age of the pet also need to be taken into account. Whilst many sick hamsters nowadays can be treated by either medication or surgery, there are unfortunately those who have incurable diseases or are suffering due to old age and its related problems where euthanasia is the kindest option.

An important factor to consider is whether there are any health risks to the owner. Some diseases such as ringworm may be potentially treatable for the hamster. However, the risk of spread of the disease to the owner and especially to children often dictates that euthanasia be the preferred option.

Should euthanasia be requested just because the pet is unwanted or that a member of the household has developed an allergy to them, then alternatives to euthanasia should be explored. It is incredibly sad to put a healthy creature to sleep through no fault of its own. See if a friend will offer a home to it. If the hamster is still young, the pet shop where it was purchased might agree to accept it back for resale. A notice could perhaps be put up in your veterinary surgery or, if necessary, you could take your pet to a pet rescue centre or the RSPCA.

Method of Euthanasia
The process of euthanasia is essentially painless, often other than a tiny prick of the injection. All pets that are put to sleep are treated with respect and dignity. Euthanasia is usually via an overdose of a general anaesthetic administered either as a sweet gas to breathe or a painless injection of a liquid anaesthetic.

The whole procedure is kept as quiet and stress free as possible to reduce upset to both the animal and the owner. The anaesthetic causes the breathing to cease and heart to slow down and stop. Some post mortem reflexes such as deep breaths or twitching may occur after death has taken place. These are perfectly normal and do not mean the animal is still alive.

Euthanasia should only be carried out by a veterinary surgeon. Should you know in advance that this would be the purpose of your visit to the veterinary surgery, it worth informing the receptionist when booking the appointment. Your appointment will then normally be at a time when the surgery is quietest and a longer appointment time may be allocated. Most veterinary surgeons are perfectly happy to have adult owners present at the time of euthanasia if so requested. It is inadvisable, however, to have children present at this time as emotional problems may arise later.

The dying hamster
The perfect way for any pet to die would be for them to go peacefully and painlessly in their sleep at a good old age at home. Sadly, this is not always the case. Hamsters often develop illnesses leading to long-term suffering. The 'natural' process of dying from old age may become protracted and distressing for both the pet and the owner. Should your hamster be peacefully fading away, dying from old age, and clearly be in no distress, then leave them in their nest to die peacefully. Move any food containers and water bottles to within easy reach of them so they don't have to climb to another level or compartment in order to eat or drink. You might want to provide them with easy to eat food such as pureed vegetables or baby rice. Water can be dripped into their mouth from a syringe so they don't dehydrate.

It would be wrong to think that a 'natural' death is necessarily always pleasant. Watching a pet linger as each bodily function starts to deteriorate can be distressing for all concerned. Some animals take only a day or two to die of old age whilst others can linger for a week or even longer. Your pet may also suffer pain from pressure sores and urine scalds that develop as its body deteriorates. The fighting spirit and the will to live that so many of these small animals have is incredible but it is also very distressing for the owner to see them like this, desperately holding onto every minute. If after a few days they are still lingering, then euthanasia may be the kindest option.

Anthropomorphism

Humans often try to apply our own personalities, characteristics and feelings to animals. This is called anthropomorphism and often leads us to draw entirely the wrong conclusions from our observations of animal behaviour. It can be difficult for us to understand that a sick animal in the wild is a risk to the remainder of the pack. It slows the pack down when they move and may be a source of disease. Thus, in a wild situation, it is logical for sick individuals to be banished from the colony and left to die away from the others, taking their illnesses with them. Colony animals recognise when one of them is sick and automatically shun them. They cannot afford to bring disease into the nest.

Dying pet hamsters tend to follow these natural instincts of their wild forefathers and to leave their nest. In captivity, dead and dying animals will often be found lying away in the corner on the wood chippings rather than tucked up in the nest.

When keeping several dwarf hamsters together, this behaviour pattern is helpful in the detection of the sick animal. It might be picked on by the others and made to sleep away from the rest of the group. Veterinary advice should be sought as soon as possible in these cases to establish the cause and severity of the illness. Should the animal be dying, euthanasia to accelerate a process that is happening anyway might be recommended. This may be preferable to a slow and undignified death, which would otherwise ensue, following the natural laws of the wild.

Burial or Cremation?

Burial at home or cremation are the two standard options when dealing with disposal of the body of a dead pet. These same choices apply whether the pet has died at home naturally or via euthanasia at the veterinary surgery.

Some owners prefer to retain the bodies of their pets and to bury them at home in the garden. The body can be wrapped in cloth or placed in a homemade coffin fashioned from cardboard packaging. Custom-made wooden pet coffins are available complete with cloth linings and brass nameplates. Never bury your hamster wrapped in plastic because this delays decomposition of the body after burial. Disturbance of the grave by foxes or other animals who may detect and dig up the body is the major disadvantage of home burial. Burial should be as deep as possible and a covering of rocks or paving stones should be placed over the top to reduce these worries. A second disadvantage is that your pet will be left behind if you move house. Some owners find the presence of their pet's grave in their garden a comfort while others just find this distressing, especially where the bereavement was traumatic. The sad memories of the ailing pet may just keep being relived whenever the grave is viewed.

The alternative is to ask your veterinary surgery to arrange a cremation for your pet. The body will normally be retained at the surgery from where a crematorium will collect it. Individual cremation can be requested although this may be expensive. In this case, your pet's ashes are returned to you in a wooden casket with the pets name inscribed on a brass plaque. The ashes may then be buried, sprinkled or the casket retained as a permanent memorial.

Burial Ceremony

When the pet has belonged to a child, then a burial ceremony of some sort may be advisable to allow an opportunity to say goodbye. This helps the child come to terms with the finality of death. Such ceremonies help the child emotionally to move on. Should you wish to plant a flower or shrub over their grave or in their memory, evergreen plants are best since deciduous plants can look extremely sad in the winter when they have died back. Remembrance plaques can also be purchased to mark the grave. Such memorials can equally be used to commemorate a valued pet that has been cremated.

It is a common misconception by persons who have never owned a hamster that, since these are such small animals and live for such a short time, strong emotional bonds do not develop with them. In truth, anyone who has ever offered a home to a hamster will know how close one can get to them and the tremendous relationship that develops. The death of a hamster can be extremely traumatic for the owner. The grieving process may be as severe as any seen following the loss of a human friend or family member. This should never be overlooked or trivialised.

Post Mortem

There are occasions when it will be helpful to perform a post mortem. Examples would include colony or multi-hamster households where a post-mortem on an early casualty may assist in treatment or disease prevention for the remaining animals. Even where there is only one pet in the household, it may help you to come to terms with the loss of your pet to know for definite the cause of death.

There are two main types of post mortem. The first is a gross post mortem where your veterinary surgeon will examine the body grossly for obvious signs of cause of death. The second is a complete gross and microbiological/ histopathological post mortem where the examination also includes sampling various organs from the body for later laboratory analysis. These tests obviously will add greatly to the expense of the post mortem but identification of the true cause of death is more likely.

It is important to remember that a post mortem will involve opening the body of the hamster. Thus, it may be better to request your veterinary surgeon to arrange cremation afterwards to avoid distress, especially to children, by taking such a body for a home burial.

Chapter 10

Further Reading and Useful Addresses

Further Reading

Exotic Animal Formulary
By James W. Carpenter, Ted Y. Mashima and David J. Rupiper
Published by W. B. Saunders Company
ISBN 0 7216 8312 6

Ferrets, Rabbits and Rodents
By Elizabeth V. Hillyer and Katherine E. Quesenberry
Published by W. B. Saunders Company
ISBN 0 7216 4023 0

Exotic DVM Veterinary Magazine
Published by Zoological Education Network, 5700 Lake Worth Road, Suite 107, Lake Worth, FL 33463, USA

Diseases of Small Domestic Rodents
By V. C. G. Richardson
Published by Blackwell Science
ISBN 0 632 04132-3

The Veterinary Formulary
Edited by Yolande Bishop
Published by the British Veterinary Association and the Royal
Pharmaceutical Society ISBN 0 85369 345 5

BSAVA Manual of Exotic Pets
Edited by Peter H. Beynon and John E. Cooper
Published by the British Small Animal Veterinary Association
ISBN 0 905214 15 3

Compendium of Data Sheets for Veterinary Products
By National Office of Animal Health Ltd,
3 Crossfield Chambers, Gladbeck Way,
Enfield, Middlesex EN2 7HF
ISBN 0 9526638 6 4

Ask the Vet Exotic Pets
By David L. Williams
Published by Lifelearn Limited
ISBN 0 9532889 0 0

Self-Assessment Colour Review of Small Mammals
By Susan A. Brown and Karen L. Rosenthal
Published by Manson Publishing
ISBN 1 874545 45 6

The Henston Small Animal Veterinary Vade Mecum
Designed and produced by Veterinary Business Development
Published by Henston Veterinary Publications
ISBN 1 85054 122 1

Homeopathy - First Aid for Pets
By Christopher Day MA VetMB MRCVS VetFFHom
Published by Chinham Publications

A Guide to the Homeopathic Treatment of Pets, Birds and Wild Animals
By Christopher Day MA VetMB MRCVS VetFFHom
Published by Chinham Publications (in preparation)

The Homeopathic Treatment of Small Animals - Principles and Practice - 3rd Edition
By Christopher Day MA VetMB MRCVS VetFFHom
Published by C W Daniel

Bach Flower Remedies for Animals
By Stefan Ball and Judy Howard
Published by C W Daniel

Aloe Vera Natures Gift
Aloe Vera in Veterinary Practice
By David Urch BSc MA VetMB MRCVS
Published by Blackdown Publications

Useful Addresses

Dan O Neill MVB BSc(hons) MRCVS
Allpets Veterinary Clinic
10 Station Square
Petts Wood
Kent BR5 1NA
Tel/Fax: 01689 834109

The Bach Centre
Mount Vernon
Sotwell
Wallingford
Oxon, OX10 0PZ
Tel: 01491 834678
www.bachcentre.com

Forever Living Products (UK) Limited (Suppliers of Aloe
Vera Products)
Longbridge Manor
Longbridge
Warwick, CV34 6RB
Tel: 01926 408800

**British Association of Homeopathic Veterinary
Surgeons**
Hon. Sec. Alternative Veterinary Medicine Centre
Chinham House
Stanford in the Vale
Oxon SN7 8NQ
Tel: 01367 718115/710324

British Small Animal Veterinary Association
Woodrow House
1 Telford Way
Waterwells Business Park
Quedgeley
Gloucester GL2 4AB
Tel: 01452 726700

British Hamster Association
P O Box 825
Sheffield, S17 3RU

Royal Society for the Prevention of Cruelty to Animals
Head Office
Causeway
Horsham
West Sussex RH12 1HG
Tel: 01403 264181

Appendix 1

A guide to the dietary sources of vitamins and minerals

	Vitamin A	Vitamin B	Vitamin C	Vitamin D	Vitamin E	Vitamin K	Potassium	Zinc	Calcium	
Apple	•		•				•			
Brocolli	•	•	•			•	•		•	
Brussels Sprouts	•	•	•			•	•			
Cabbage	•	•	•			•	•		•	
Carrots	•	•					•			
Dandelion leaves	•	•	•	•		•	•	•	•	
Grapes	•		•				•			
Green beans	•		•				•			
Monkey nuts					•		•			
Nuts					•		•			
Orange			•				•			
Parsley	•	•	•				•		•	
Peppers	•		•							
Pumpkin seeds					•			•	•	
Peas		•	•		•	•	•	•		
Raisons/dried fruit										
Sesame seeds									•	
Spinach	•	•	•				•			
Sunflower seeds		•			•		•			
Sweet corn								•		
Watercress	•	•	•		•	•	•		•	
Wheat germ		•			•					

Iron	Biotin	MAgnesium	Manganese	Chromium	Folic Acid	Selenium	Essntial	Protein
		•		•				
			•		•	•		
					•			
	•	•	•		•	•		
•		•	•					
•								•
•								•
								•
•		•						
				•				
•			•				•	•
•	•	•						
•		•	•				•	•
•		•	•		•			
	•						•	•
	•							
•		•	•					
		•			•			

Appendix II

First aid kit

As with all pets, accidents, injuries and illness can occur at any time of the day or night. With small pets, especially nocturnal ones, you may not notice anything wrong until the evening. Whilst it will be necessary for some situations to get your pet to the vet immediately, some conditions can be treated at home. It is therefore helpful to keep a first aid kit, just in case of emergency.

Contents of a first aid kit

The types of things to keep in a first aid kit are:

Syringes - different sizes for measuring medication or feeding animals who are too poorly to take solid food. You can get these either from the vet or chemist. Dropper bottles are also handy.

Tweezers - can be used for untangling caught fur or other delicate procedures or removal of irritant conjunctival foreign bodies such as sawdust.

Nail clippers - can be used for trimming nails and teeth. If you think your hamster has overgrown teeth or nails take them to the vet in the first instance. If this is likely to be done regularly, the vet will show you how to cut them without causing pain to your pet. It is important not to trim teeth or nails too short, or you may cause bleeding and unnecessary discomfort.

Silver nitrate sticks or ferric chloride - this can be used if your hamster's nails have been cut too short and they bleed. This can be purchased from your chemist.

Microwaveable heat pad - this can be placed to one side of the nest to help retain body heat in a sick animal. It should be well covered to avoid burning the hamster. Beware of placing very sick hamsters on microwaveable heat pads as they may be too sick to move even if they are overheating.

Bach Flower Remedies: Rescue™ Remedy, Walnut, Star of Bethlehem. These remedies (and others) help treat emotional symptoms and can be purchased in chemists or health stores. See Chapter 8 for more details.

Tea Tree cream is an excellent antiseptic for putting on cuts and scratches and can work extremely quickly. It can be purchased from the pet shop in a potency specially designed for small animals. Due to its strong smell, however, if you keep more than one hamster in the same tank it is a good idea to put a small dab of cream on the other hamsters to prevent them turning against the one being treated.

Aloe Vera - in gel or spray form. Ideal for treating skin conditions and scratches. Ensure it is safe if ingested.

Vitamin drops - purchased from pet shops.

Echinacea - can be bought in herbal tincture form. This is available in 'alcohol free' variety. If using a tincture containing alcohol, put the drops in a spoonful of hot (boiled) water to allow the alcohol to evaporate before adding it to your hamster's water bottle. Some brands have a bitter taste and may need sweetening slightly to encourage your hamster to drink.

Evening primrose oil - can be purchased in dropper bottles, which is more cost efficient than in capsules when treating pets. Put a drop on fresh food placed in the cage each day for hamsters with skin conditions. It is a valuable dietary supplement, particularly affecting hormonal and skin health.

Arnica - This homeopathic remedy will help to treat any injury, minimising bruising and tissue damage. Other first-aid remedies may be required, according to the specific nature of the injury (see below), but Arnica will always help healing and pain relief - one tablet crushed and dissolved in the water bottle is excellent for helping relieve any bruising if your pet has had an accident or undergone surgery.

Other homeopathic remedies that you might wish to include in your first aid kit are as follows. Descriptions of these remedies can be found in Chapter 8.

Aconite
Hypericum
Ledum
Calendula Lotion
Carbo veg.
Ruta graveolens
Natrum sulph.
Hepar sulph.
Secale
Euphrasia
Symphytum

Electrolyte mixtures such as Lectade are useful forms of rehydration.

Hospitalisation or isolation cage to give warmth and individual treatment, see Chapter 1 'Reintroduction of Hamsters'.

Emergency pain relief can be achieved using aspirin and ibuprofen.

Instructions for dosage and use of drugs and remedies mentioned in this Appendix can be found in Chapter 8.

Appendix III

The table on the following pages is a quick and handy cross reference to help you find some likely causes for symptoms your hamster is showing.

Simply select the symptom from the vertical column along the left hand side and then read across the squares to see some possible causes. For further information on the disease, go to the relevant section in Chapter 7.

SYMPTOMS

	Scent Glands	Tooth root abcess	Everted pouch	Polyomavirus	Glaucoma	Wheel Rubs	Ringworm	Mange	Abscess	Allergy	Pregnant	Giving Birth	Ovarian Cysts
Baldness	•					•	•	•		•			
Sore skin along back							•	•		•			
Sore skin inside legs						•	•	•	•	•			
Sore eye					•		•	•		•			
Not eating		•	•	•	•				•			•	•
Diarrhoea				•									
Vulval Discharge											•	•	•
Weight Loss		•		•									
Limping													
Lump on Skin		•		•					•				
Severe Dullness		•		•	•				•				
Swollen cheeks		•	•						•				
Swollen Abdomen				•					•		•	•	•
Wheezing/laboured breathing				•							•	•	•
Increased thirst													
Difficulty eating/drooling		•	•		•				•				
Malodour to body		•	•				•	•	•				
Oral mass visible		•	•						•				
Thickened skin						•	•	•	•	•			
"Sudden death"				•									
Collapse									•			•	
Straining												•	
Bloody milk												•	

216

SYMPTOMS

Symptom	Pyometra	Bladder	Kidney failure	Overgrown teeth	Impacted cheek pouches	Wet Tail	Twisted Bowel	Rectal prolapse	Constipation	Age related respiratory infect.	Hay fever	Conjunctivitus	Eye prolapse
Baldness			•										
Sore skin along back													
Sore skin inside legs													
Sore eye											•	•	•
Not eating	•	•	•	•	•	•	•	•	•	•			
Diarrhoea						•	•	•	•	•			
Vulval Discharge	•												
Weight Loss	•		•	•		•				•			
Limping													
Lump on Skin													
Severe Dullness	•	•	•			•	•	•	•	•			
Swollen cheeks				•	•								
Swollen Abdomen	•						•	•	•	•			
Wheezing/laboured breathing										•	•		
Increased thirst			•										
Difficulty eating/drooling				•	•								
Malodour to body	•	•		•	•								
Oral mass visible													
Thickened skin													
"Sudden death"	•		•				•	•	•				
Collapse	•		•				•	•	•		•		
Straining							•	•	•	•			
Bloody milk													

217

SYMPTOMS	Cataract	Fractured leg	Nail overgrowth	Cage paralysis	Hibernation	Diabetes	Tumour	Age related	Ear mites	Tyzzer's Disease	Antibiotic Diarrhoea	Dietary Diarrhoea	Yersinia
Baldness							•	•	•				
Sore skin along back									•				
Sore skin inside legs									•				
Sore eye	•								•				
Not eating				•			•			•			
Diarrhoea										•	•	•	•
Vulval Discharge													
Weight Loss						•	•			•	•	•	•
Limping		•	•	•									
Lump on Skin							•						
Severe Dullness		•		•	•		•			•	•	•	•
Swollen cheeks									•				
Swollen Abdomen							•			•			
Wheezing/laboured breathing							•						
Increased thirst	•					•							
Difficulty eating/drooling							•						
Malodour to body										•	•	•	•
Oral mass visible							•						
Thickened skin									•				
"Sudden death"			•	•	•		•			•	•	•	•
Collapse				•	•		•			•	•		•
Straining										•	•	•	•
Bloody milk													

SYMPTOMS	Colds	Heart Failure	Mastitus	Pregnancy	Tourniquet	Heat Stroke	Chocolate Toxicity	Obesity	Aspergillosis	Intestinal Parasites
Baldness								•		
Sore skin along back										
Sore skin inside legs										
Sore eye	•									
Not eating	•	•		•		•	•			
Diarrhoea							•		•	
Vulval Discharge										
Weight Loss		•	•	•						•
Limping						•			•	
Lump on Skin						•				
Severe Dullness		•	•	•	•	•	•	•	•	
Swollen cheeks										
Swollen Abdomen		•		•					•	•
Wheezing/laboured breathing	•	•		•		•		•	•	
Increased thirst										
Difficulty eating/drooling	•									
Malodour to body										
Oral mass visible										
Thickened skin										
"Sudden death"		•		•		•	•		•	
Collapse		•		•		•	•			
Straining										
Bloody milk			•							

Index

A selection of other titles published by Capall Bann:

Eternally - Yours Faithfully Roy Radford and Evelyn Gregory

"...sure to be a comfort to all those who have ever lost a much-loved pet...sensitively written, this book will appeal to all animal lovers and provide consolation to those bereaved by the death of a pet." Your Cat Magazine

Based upon the personal experiences of many people from the UK and around the world, the authors consider many thought provoking issues concerning pets within these pages: Are our dearest pets angels in disguise? Encounters across the Rainbow Bridge - the personal experiences of people who no longer doubt that their past beloved pets return to them and that their present pets receive the approval, or even the guidance, of some among the dearly loved who have passed over; Trust and Loyalty know no barriers - physical or spiritual; Can a human find a kindred spirit in a pet?; are we chosen by the pet - are their needs more important to us than we imagine? A fascinating, thought-provoking and meaningful book for anyone who has ever loved a pet. Lovely illustrations by Lin Bourne. ISBN 186163 1049   £10.95

Your Talking Pet Ann Walker

Your Talking Pet is about 'companion animals', the cats and dogs who live in our houses and are called 'pets'. For various reasons, we selected these two species to share our homes and our lives and the result is a mutual dependency; they on us for their well-being, we on them for companionship, love and even to boost our self esteem. Sometimes there is a total misunderstanding between us, at others we share a bond that is as strong as any we have with our own kind. Packed with interesting facts and real-life stories, some funny and some sad, this book about people and pets will strike a chord in the heart of everyone who has ever lived with, and loved, a cat or a dog. ISBN 1898307 873   £8.95

The Mystic Life of Animals Ann Walker

"..refreshing...a wealth of information. Anyone with a love for an animal will benefit from this book, or at least know they are not crazy when they believe their animal speaks to them...Well done Ann. Recommended for all." Spiritual Links (Australia)

As the New Age moves upon us, we will increasingly recognise animals as spiritual beings worthy of our respect. "Communication is the golden key that unlocks the door to understanding." Animal communication is mostly concerned with emotions, feelings, events and happenings in the here and now. We tend to think that animal communication involves them understanding what we want, but in truth, it is a two-way process. A lifetime of living with and loving animals has led Ann Walker to conclude that much communication with animals is on a mind to mind level, and she tells of many personal psychic experiences with animals. Old superstitions and magical beliefs about animals are examined, also the attitude of different religions. Ann shares her own experiences and those of others with dead pets returning or sending messages and expresses a firm belief in the continued spiritual existence of animals after death.
ISBN 1861630166   £7.95

Cats' Company - A book of cats & - history - healing - communication - stories Ann Walker

"Quite simply, a must for cat lovers.. a well written, enjoyable book which portrays our feline friends with the reverence that they deserve" Dragons Brew

This book includes tales of cats who returned to their owners after death, both in spirit and reincarnated form. Stating that "The Ancient Celts believed that the eyes of a cat were windows through which humans could explore the inner world", we are given an extract from a grimoire giving guidance on how to attune yourself to your cat. Believing in the healing power of cats and our ability to think/talk with them, Ann shares many stories of the cats she has known and loved over the years. A fascinating and enthralling book for cat lovers everywhere. ISBN 1898307 32 6 £10.95

Gardening For Wildlife Ron Wilson

"If you have only one wildlife book, this is the one to have. The information contained in this book is invaluable. A very interesting read for young and old alike, to which you will always refer." The Professional Gardener   *"..a real delight...a fascinating read...all of the methods I have tried so far have gleaned superb results"* Touchstone   *"lively, colloquial style...quick and easy to read...inspiring and full of helpful tips'* Place

"..a nice book...lively drawings which clearly illustrate techniques...covers everything...a good starter book" Permaculture

A few 'modifications' and additions could enhance the value of most gardens for wildlife. That is what this book is all about. It offers practical advice and ideas for improvements and where possible suggests the inclusion of 'extra' features which will support and encourage a rich diversity of plant, insect, bird and animal life. Plants, foods and features are all described in plain English. Everything in this book is explained in straightforward terms to enable anyone to help their local wildlife. ISBN 1 86163 011 5   £10.95

The Magical Lore of Cats Marion Davies

The cat has a dual nature, that of the gentle, loving bundle, purring on your lap and as a predator, a character so strong that people either love cats dearly or claim to dislike them thoroughly. In Ancient Egypt the cat became an archetype for instruction and understanding. Included in the book are sections on: cats and astrology, the Celtic cat, links between cats and serpents, the relationships between cats, the moon and sun and also cats in fable, folklore and superstition with legends and stories gathered from all over the world. A wonderful book for cat lovers and those who appreciate the mysterious side of the cat. ISBN 1898307 66 0   £10.95

The Magical Lore of Animals Yvonne Aburrow

A wealth of magical animal lore at your fingertips. Yvonne gives us the magical and mythical associations, symbolism, varieties, folklore and correspondences of the animal kingdom - not just mammals, but insects, reptiles, fish, mythical beasts and even molluscs - in an easy to look up, very readable, alphabetical form. A very substantial tome by the author of the internationally acclaimed *"Enchanted Forest - The Magical Lore of Trees"* and other titles in the Capall Bann range. Features over 100 lovely illustrations by Dena Moore. ISBN 1898307 806   £18.95

Lore of the Sacred Horse - The Magical Lore of Horses

Marion Davies

"well worth reading...you would find it hard to put down" Touchstone

This noble animal has been food & transport, the innocent participant in Man's wars, at one time his Deity & the honoured companion of his Deities. The symbol of majesty & power. From seed-time to harvest, the horse has been at the forefront of agricultural economy. This book traces this relationship from earliest times, stressing the religio-magical aspects. Topics covered include: Horse Magic, Horse Cults, Horse Whisperers, Secret Societies, The Hobby Horse - Horse Festivals & Celebrations, Superstition & Folklore, Toadmen & more. ISBN 1898307 17 2   £10.95

The Enchanted Forest - The Magical Lore of Trees

Yvonne Aburrow

"..wonderful insight...easy to read...very informative, a lovely enchanting book". Touchstone *(OBOD)*

Fascinating & truly unique - a comprehensive guide to the magical, medicinal & craft uses, mythology, folklore, symbolism & weatherlore of trees. There are chapters on trees in myth & legend, tree spirits, trees in ritual magic, trees & alphabets (runes & Ogham) & weather lore. These chapters are followed by a comprehensive 'herbal index' with in-depth coverage of individual trees from acacia to aspen, wayfaring tree to willow. Profusely illustrated.

ISBN 1898307 083   £10.95

The Way the Cookie Crumbles   Malcolm Kidd

"...source of considerable interest.... lively confessions.... strong thread of humour.... hearty laughter inspired by minor misfortunes and amiable eccentricities." The Keswick Reminder

Introducing himself as a "mail order cattle salesman" - in addition to farming, Malcolm Kidd has had a full and colourful life, meeting 'worthies' and rogues in abundance. He describes his boyhood on the farm, and six wartime years in the army where he managed to start at the top and work his way down! Country tales of local squires, gamekeepers and poachers are nostalgic and often humourous. The book is illustrated with numerous period photographs. ISBN 186163 1529 £10.95

In Pursuit of Perennial Profit - The Pot of Gold at the Bottom of the Garden

Patrick Vickery

Shows how to make your garden productive in a variety of ways, for both expert and gardening novice alike, at minimum cost and in an innovative and self-financing way. For those who know little or nothing about gardening this will start you on your way, for it is not just the physical garden and it's ever-changing visual appeal that's exciting, but the journey to that end which holds the real excitement - a journey of discovery and self-fulfilment. Choosing plants to grow, organising time and space (you don't need much of either!), deterring slugs, getting the best from the plants and even how to sell excess plants should you wish are all covered here. The author writes from real experience, growing plants in the not always ideal location of Ross-shire in Scotland, as he says ""if I can do it, anybody can".

ISBN 186163 1480   £7.95

The Magical History of the Horse

Janet Farrar and Virginia Russell

"...a comprehensive guide to all aspects of horse mythology and folklore.." Prediction

This book traces the magical history of the horse throughout the centuries and explores its connections with paganism, mythology, Biblical and Christian lore, folklore and fairytale, healing and superstition. Loved, feared or venerated, the horse has become integrated with human work, warfare, history and sport. It has become the living symbol of many gods and goddesses, the prototype of many mythical beasts. Janet Farrar, established writer on magic and mythology and Virginia Russell, a lifelong horsewoman, combine their talents in this exploration of the horse's magical history. A veritable harvest of the legends, magical concepts and folk beliefs that have surrounded the horse from the dawn of history. ISBN 186163 033 6   £10.95

FREE detailed catalogue

Contact: Capall Bann Publishing
Auton Farm
Milverton
Somerset
TA4 1NE